Dreamthorp

A BOOK OF ESSAYS WRITTEN
IN THE COUNTRY

Dreamthorp

A BOOK OF ESSAYS WRITTEN
IN THE COUNTRY

By
Alexander Smith, 1830?-1867

With an introduction by
CHRISTOPHER MORLEY

MCMXXXIV
Doubleday, Doran & Company, Inc.
Garden City, New York

PRINTED AT THE *Country Life Press*, GARDEN CITY, N. Y., U. S. A.

CONTENTS

v

A LETTER TO FRANK C. HENRY
(Godfather of This New Edition)

Dear Frank:

THERE is the right moment for everything, if we are lucky enough to hit upon it, and when I was grubbing in the garden this hot afternoon I suddenly forgave myself for having so long postponed the note I promised you about *Dreamthorp*. I was rooting out weeds and underbrush and poison ivy in a small clearing, before planting grass seed there; and having had long experience with *toxicodendron* I hunted out an old pair of gloves for handling the long trailing roots. And as I grunted on all fours in a rich drip of sweat I was amused to remember that those gloves formerly belonged to a publisher friend of ours, one of the most luxurious exquisites and bibliophiles of his generation. Somehow, I thought, the fact that those once elegant kids could be used to grapple poison ivy would have pleased

vii

Alexander Smith. Even *Dreamthorp*, so quiet and tender a book, also takes hold of some bitter and stinging themes.

I was happy, as one can't help being when on fours with earth, and thinking of *Dreamthorp* my mind went back to an English garden where, exactly thirty years ago, I used to watch my grandfather amuse himself spudding up weeds. How different was his fine English lawn from my own bumpy and shabby turf. I can see him plainly, kneeling on a copy of the *Standard* and slicing out with a penknife small weeds which I myself would now gratefully think of as grass. In the self-centered assurance of fourteen years I don't suppose it ever occurred to me to wonder what went through his mind as he spent his last summer days on the lawn. He had known George Meredith, and was at one time a director of the firm that published Dickens; I daresay he could have told me something about Alexander Smith, for he was a young man at the time of Smith's great vogue as the coming poet. But we are heedless little animals at that age; only some colossal event —such as Smith describes in the famous horror sketch *A Lark's Flight*—can break through a boy's intense occupation with his own private excitements.

I found myself wondering what Alexander Smith would have thought of the queer little clump of Long Island jungle where I was enjoying myself. He would have envied me the catbirds, so tame

that when you begin raking or scraping about they
follow close behind looking for what you turn up.
He would be amused by their behavior this thirsty
weather: if you forget to fill the bird-bath they
come and hover about the house to advertise
you that something is wrong. It is always pleasant
to look out from the bathroom (there's a window
alongside the tub) and see a catbird taking his
morning splash at the same time I do. That particular fowl, I think, stays up late at night. This
afternoon I saw three birds politely taking their
baths in turn. A catbird flew down, found a robin
already in the basin, turned away with a quick
gesture of apology, and waited. Meanwhile a
sparrow, smallest of the three, stood prudently
aside till both the others were through.

The trim intelligent catbird with his dark
shrewd eye is perhaps a parable of the reader of
this book. When Alexander Smith wanders about
Dreamthorp, or when he talks of his library
shelves, he turns up surprising nourishment. He
is worth following closely. His essays are of an
older fashion but no one has ever spoken more
pleasantly of the essayist's purpose and privilege,
or of the perplexities of the life of letters. And I
need not apologize for mentioning my own small
concerns of poison ivy and grass seed since Smith
so winningly reminds us of the suggestiveness of
common things. In this sad and delightful book
he made himself the amanuensis of a Scottish
village. He disguised it carefully, but when he

speaks of twilight lasting until 11 p.m. we know it must have been Scotland.

A sad book, I found myself saying: it has the delicious gift of melancholy. In all the years I have loved this book I have never cared much to identify Dreamthorp itself (very likely it is largely imaginary) nor to rummage out the details of Smith's life. That he was born in Kilmarnock, abandoned a notion of entering the church, was famous as a poet in his early twenties, and became secretary of Edinburgh University, is all that sticks in my mind. All the comments on him that I have ever seen say that he "died of overwork." What, then: this delicious picture of indolence and ease, loafing about the village, gardening, reading, is it all fiction? The pose as an old gentleman is also fiction, for we know that he was only 34 when this book was published—and died at 36. I can't help getting a grin when he speaks—in the essay on *Death and the Fear of Dying*—of the man of thirty as such an aged veteran.

Which reminds me of one of our latest converts in our long secret campaign to win new readers for this dear old book. You remember when our friend Joe Jackson, literary critic in San Francisco, was about to fly back from New York to California by plane. He was a bit nervous about it, for there had been several bad crashes on the transcontinental route. Thinking of the more bookish chapters you gave Joe a copy, telling him that he would probably be the first man in

the world ever to read *Dreamthorp* in the sky,
en route toward the sunset Smith always pursued
with such subtle pen. But when Mr. Jackson
opened the book 5000 feet in air the first thing
his eye fell upon was "Death—and the Fear of
Dying;" and read "Your death and my death are
mainly of importance to ourselves. The black
plumes will be stripped off our hearses within the
hour . . . the world does not miss us. . . ."

Mr. Jackson wrote us about it quite gaily—after
he was safe in San Francisco.

I take the liberty of setting down this little
note in the form of a letter to you, old son, because
it is your faithful affection for it that has made
possible this edition of our own; and because it
was one of the first books in which you and I
found a common agreement. We discovered it
separately and far apart: you, if I remember, as
a youngster working at Lauriat's bookstore in
Boston; I by reading of it in Thomas B. Mosher's
excellent old *Bibelot* series. In the summer of 1913
Mosher reprinted (from the *Yellow Book* of 1895)
an essay by James Ashcroft Noble entitled *Mr.
Stevenson's Forerunner*. In those days I was in
the culmination of a strong Stevensonian fever; I
was immediately astounded—even piqued—to
imagine that R. L. S. could have had a "forerunner," and hastened to read the piece. I found
that Mr. Noble was to some extent justified in his
title; for in Stevenson's youthful fragment *Lay
Morals*, and the famous *Apology for Idlers*, are

interesting parallels to what Smith said on *Vagabonds*—the talk at the Dreamthorp Literary Institute, which made even the "atrabilious confectioner" clap his hands.

I have written several pages and said very
little; at least I haven't dulled the edge of the
reader's pleasure by quoting slabs of Alexander
Smith's closely knit thinking. Here we are made
free of one of the most charming of little-known
classics. The only immortality Smith hoped for
(he says somewhere) was "to be quoted occasionally." Let none be deceived by his pretended
posture of seniority: this is a young man's book;
young even in its instinctive return to sombre
themes. It is odd that teachers have not made
more use of it; it has extraordinarily fine things
to say about literature, things almost worthy of
Lamb; and he introduces his ironies so quietly
that you might almost think them not ironical
but just Scotch. "To be publicly put to death
must be a serious matter." And finally, in *Dreamthorp* the enthusiast has one of the most selfish
refinements of booklovers' delight: it is a book that
only the very few have ever heard of. This edition
has been set from a copy of the first edition (1863)
and the text is exactly as it left Smith's pen.

He belongs on the shelf with those very special
favorites of the tenderest passion—with Lamb and
Hunt and Hazlitt and *Ryecroft;* with Sir Roger
and *Walden* and Santayana. Or perhaps with that
supremely Scottish classic, now too much for-

gotten, Galt's *Annals of the Parish*. If you were to put him not too far away from his idol Montaigne then (in the words of the younger Scot) "There he lies where he longed to be." Some day I must look up his biography. I can't quite believe that a man so wise would allow himself to be killed "of overwork." Let us remember that!

Affectionately yours,
CHRISTOPHER MORLEY.

July 19, 1934.

Dreamthorp

A BOOK OF ESSAYS WRITTEN
IN THE COUNTRY

DREAMTHORP

IT MATTERS not to relate how or when I became a denizen of Dreamthorp; it will be sufficient to say that I am not a born native, but that I came to reside in it a good while ago now. The several towns and villages in which, in my time, I have pitched a tent did not please, for one obscure reason or another: this one was too large, t'other too small; but when, on a summer evening about the hour of eight, I first beheld Dreamthorp, with its westward-looking windows painted by sunset, its children playing in the single straggling street, the mothers knitting at the open doors, the fathers standing about in long white blouses, chatting or smoking; the great tower of the ruined castle rising high into the rosy air, with a whole troop of swallows—by distance made as small as gnats—skimming about its rents and fissures;— when I first beheld all this, I felt instinctively that my knapsack might be taken off my shoulders, that my tired feet might wander no more, that at last, on the planet, I had found a home. From that evening I have dwelt here, and the only journey I am like now to make, is the very inconsiderable one, so far at least as distance is concerned, from the house in which I live to the graveyard beside the ruined castle. There, with the former inhabitants of the place, I trust to sleep quietly enough, and nature will draw over our heads her coverlet of green sod, and tenderly tuck us in, as a mother her sleeping ones, so that no sound from the world shall ever reach us, and no sorrow trouble us any more.

The village stands far inland; and the streams that trot through the soft green valleys all about have as little knowledge of the sea, as the three-years' child of the storms and passions of manhood. The surrounding country is smooth and green, full of undulations; and pleasant country roads strike through it in every direction, bound for distant towns and villages, yet in no hurry to reach them. On these roads the lark in summer is continually heard; nests are plentiful in the hedges and dry ditches; and on the grassy banks, and at the feet of the bowed dikes, the blue-eyed speedwell smiles its benison on the passing wayfarer. On these roads you may walk for a year and encounter nothing more remarkable than the country cart, troops of tawny children from the woods, laden with primroses, and at long intervals—for people in this district live to a ripe age—a black funeral creeping in from some remote hamlet; and to this last the people reverently doff their hats and stand aside. Death does not walk about here often, but when he does, he receives as much respect as the squire himself. Everything round one is unhurried, quiet, moss-grown, and orderly. Season follows in the track of season, and one year can hardly be distinguished from another. Time should be measured here by the silent dial, rather than by the ticking clock, or by the chimes of the church. Dreamthorp can boast of a respectable antiquity, and in it the trade of the builder is unknown. Ever since I remember, not a single stone has been laid on the top of another. The castle, inhabited now by jackdaws and starlings, is old; the chapel which adjoins it is older still; and the lake behind both, and in which their shadows sleep, is, I suppose, as old as Adam. A fountain in the market-place, all mouths and faces and curious arabesques—as dry, however, as the castle moat—has a tradition connected with it; and a great noble riding through the street one day several hundred years ago, was shot from a window by a man whom he had injured. The death of this noble is the chief link which connects the place with authentic history. The houses are old, and remote dates may yet be deciphered on the stones above the doors; the apple-trees are mossed and ancient; countless generations of sparrows have bred in the thatched roofs, and thereon have chirped out their lives. In every room of the place men have been born, men have died. On Dreamthorp centuries have fallen, and have left no more trace

than have last winter's snowflakes. This commonplace sequence and flowing on of life is immeasurably affecting. That winter morning when Charles
lost his head in front of the banqueting-hall of
his own palace, the icicles hung from the eaves
of the houses here, and the clown kicked the
snowballs from his clouted shoon, and thought
but of his supper when, at three o'clock, the red
sun set in the purple mist. On that Sunday in
June while Waterloo was going on, the gossips,
after morning service, stood on the country roads
discussing agricultural prospects, without the
slightest suspicion that the day passing over their
heads would be a famous one in the calendar.
Battles have been fought, kings have died, history has transacted itself; but, all unheeding and
untouched, Dreamthorp has watched apple-trees
redden, and wheat ripen, and smoked its pipe, and
quaffed its mug of beer, and rejoiced over its new-
born children, and with proper solemnity carried
its dead to the churchyard. As I gaze on the village of my adoption, I think of many things very
far removed, and seem to get closer to them. The
last setting sun that Shakspeare saw reddened
the windows here, and struck warmly on the faces
of the hinds coming home from the fields. The
mighty storm that raged while Cromwell lay
a-dying made all the oak-woods groan round about
here, and tore the thatch from the very roofs I
gaze upon. When I think of this, I can almost, so
to speak, lay my hand on Shakspeare and on

Cromwell. These poor walls were contemporaries
of both, and I find something affecting in the
thought. The mere soil is, of course, far older than
either, but *it* does not touch one in the same way.
A wall is the creation of a human hand, the soil
is not.

This place suits my whim, and I like it better
year after year. As with everything else, since
I began to love it I find it gradually growing beautiful. Dreamthorp—a castle, a chapel, a lake, a
straggling strip of gray houses, with a blue film
of smoke over all—lies embosomed in emerald.
Summer, with its daisies, runs up to every cottage
door. From the little height where I am now sitting, I see it beneath me. Nothing could be more
peaceful. The wind and the birds fly over it. A
passing sunbeam makes brilliant a white gable-
end, and brings out the colours of the blossomed
apple-tree beyond, and disappears. I see figures
in the street, but hear them not. The hands on
the church clock seem always pointing to one
hour. Time has fallen asleep in the afternoon sunshine. I make a frame of my fingers, and look at
my picture. On the walls of the next Academy's
Exhibition will hang nothing half so beautiful!

My village is, I think, a special favourite of
summer's. Every window-sill in it she touches
with colour and fragrance; everywhere she wakens
the drowsy murmurs of the hives; every place
she scents with apple-blossom. Traces of her
hand are to be seen on the weir beside the ruined

mill; and even the canal, along which the barges
come and go, has a great white water-lily asleep
on its olive-coloured face. Never was velvet on
a monarch's robe so gorgeous as the green mosses
that be-ruff the roofs of farm and cottage, when
the sunbeam slants on them and goes. The old
road out towards the common, and the hoary
dikes that might have been built in the reign of
Alfred, have not been forgotten by the generous
adorning season; for every fissure has its mossy
cushion, and the old blocks themselves are washed
by the loveliest gray-green lichens in the world,
and the large loose stones lying on the ground
have gathered to themselves the peacefulest mossy
coverings. Some of these have not been disturbed
for a century. Summer has adorned my village
as gaily, and taken as much pleasure in the task,
as the people of old, when Elizabeth was queen,
took in the adornment of the May-pole against
a summer festival. And, just think, not only
Dreamthorp, but every English village she has
made beautiful after one fashion or another—
making vivid green the hill slope on which straggling white Welsh hamlets hang right opposite
the sea; drowning in apple-blossom the red Sussex
ones in the fat valley. And think, once more,
every spear of grass in England she has touched
with a livelier green; the crest of every bird she
has burnished; every old wall between the four
seas has received her mossy and licheny attentions; every nook in every forest she has sown with

pale flowers, every marsh she has dashed with the fires of the marigold. And in the wonderful night the moon knows, she hangs—the planet on which so many millions of us fight, and sin, and agonise, and die—a sphere of glow-worm light.

Having discoursed so long about Dreamthorp, it is but fair that I should now introduce you to her lions. These are, for the most part, of a commonplace kind; and I am afraid that, if you wish to find romance in them, you must bring it with you. I might speak of the old church-tower, or of the church-yard beneath it, in which the village holds its dead, each resting-place marked by a simple stone, on which is inscribed the name and age of the sleeper, and a Scripture text beneath, in which live our hopes of immortality. But, on the whole, perhaps it will be better to begin with the canal, which wears on its olive-coloured face the big white water-lily already chronicled. Such a secluded place is Dreamthorp that the railway does not come near, and the canal is the only thing that connects it with the world. It stands high, and from it the undulating country may be seen stretching away into the gray of distance, with hills and woods, and stains of smoke which mark the sites of villages. Every now and then a horse comes staggering along the towing-path, trailing a sleepy barge filled with merchandise. A quiet, indolent life these barge-men lead in the summer days. One lies stretched at his length on the sun-heated plank; his comrade sits smoking in the little dog-hutch, which I suppose he calls a cabin. Silently they come and go; silently the wooden bridge lifts to let them through. The horse stops at the bridge-house for a drink, and there I like to talk a little with the men. They serve instead of a newspaper, and retail with great willingness the news they have picked up in their progress from town to town. I am told they sometimes marvel who the old gentleman is who accosts them from beneath a huge umbrella in the sun, and that they think him either very wise or very foolish. Not in the least unnatural! We are great friends, I believe—evidence of which they occasionally exhibit by requesting me to disburse a trifle for drink-money. This canal is a great haunt of mine of an evening. The water hardly invites one to bathe in it, and a delicate stomach might suspect the flavour of the eels caught therein; yet, to my thinking, it is not in the least destitute of beauty. A barge trailing up through it in the sunset is a pretty sight; and the heavenly crimsons and purples sleep quite lovingly upon its glossy ripples. Nor does the evening star disdain it, for as I walk along I see it mirrored therein as clearly as in the waters of the Mediterranean itself.

The old castle and chapel already alluded to are, perhaps, to a stranger, the points of attraction in Dreamthorp. Back from the houses is the lake, on the green sloping banks of which, with broken windows and tombs, the ruins stand. As it is noon, and the weather is warm, let us go and sit on a turret. Here, on these very steps, as old ballads tell, a queen sat once, day after day, looking southward for the light of returning spears. I bethink me that yesterday, no further gone, I went to visit a consumptive shoemaker; seated here I can single out his very house, nay, the very window of the room in which he is lying. On that straw roof might the raven alight, and flap his sable wings. There, at this moment, is the supreme tragedy being enacted. A woman is weeping there, and little children are looking on with a sore bewilderment. Before nightfall the poor peaked face of the bowed artisan will have gathered its ineffable peace, and the widow will be led away from the bedside by the tenderness of neighbours, and the cries of the orphan brood will be stilled. And yet this present indubitable suffering and loss does not touch me like the sorrow of the woman of the ballad, the phantom probably of a minstrel's brain. The shoemaker will be forgotten —I shall be forgotten; and long after visitors will sit here and look out on the landscape and murmur the simple lines. But why do death and dying obtrude themselves at the present moment? On the turret opposite, about the distance of a gunshot, is as pretty a sight as eye could wish to see. Two young people, strangers apparently, have come to visit the ruin. Neither the ballad queen, nor the shoemaker down yonder, whose respirations are getting shorter and shorter, touches them in the least. They are merry and happy, and the graybeard turret has not the heart to thrust a foolish moral upon them. They would not thank him if he did, I daresay. Perhaps they could not understand him. Time enough! Twenty years hence they will be able to sit down at his feet, and count griefs with him, and tell him tale for tale. Human hearts get ruinous in so much less time than stone walls and towers. See, the young man has thrown himself down at the girl's feet on a little space of grass. In her scarlet cloak she looks like a blossom springing out of a crevice on the ruined steps. He gives her a flower, and she bows her face down over it almost to her knees. What did the flower say? Is it to hide a blush? He looks delighted; and I almost fancy I see a proud colour on his brow. As I gaze, these young people make for me a perfect idyl. The generous, ungrudging sun, the melancholy ruin, decked, like mad Lear, with the flowers and ivies of forgetfulness and grief, and between them, sweet and evanescent, human truth and love!

Love!—does it yet walk the world, or is it imprisoned in poems and romances? Has not the circulating library become the sole home of the passion? Is love not become the exclusive property of novelists and playwrights, to be used by them only for professional purposes? Surely, if the men I see are lovers, or ever have been lovers, they would be nobler than they are. The knowledge that he is beloved should—*must* make a man

tender, gentle, upright, pure. While yet a youngster in a jacket, I can remember falling desperately in love with a young lady several years my
senior—after the fashion of youngsters in jackets.
Could I have fibbed in these days? Could I have
betrayed a comrade? Could I have stolen eggs or
callow young from the nest? Could I have stood
quietly by and seen the weak or the maimed
bullied? Nay, verily! In these absurd days she
lighted up the whole world for me. To sit in the
same room with her was like the happiness of
perpetual holiday; when she asked me to run a
message for her, or to do any, the slightest, service for her, I felt as if a patent of nobility were
conferred on me. I kept my passion to myself,
like a cake, and nibbled it in private. Juliet was
several years my senior, and had a lover—was,
in point of fact, actually engaged; and, in looking
back, I can remember I was too much in love to
feel the slightest twinge of jealousy. I remember
also seeing Romeo for the first time, and thinking
him a greater man than Caesar or Napoleon. The
worth I credited him with, the cleverness, the
goodness, the everything! He awed me by his manner and bearing. He accepted that girl's love coolly
and as a matter of course; it put him no more
about than a crown and sceptre puts about a king.
What I would have given my life to possess—being
only fourteen, it was not much to part with after
all—he wore lightly, as he wore his gloves or his
cane. It did not seem a bit too good for him.

His self-possession appalled me. If I had seen him take the sun out of the sky, and put it into his breeches' pocket, I don't think I should have been in the least degree surprised. Well, years after, when I had discarded my passion with my jacket, I have assisted this middle-aged Romeo home from a roystering wine-party, and heard him hiccup out his marital annoyances, with the strangest remembrances of old times, and the strangest deductions therefrom. Did that man with the idiotic laugh and the blurred utterance ever love? Was he ever capable of loving? I protest I have my doubts. But where are my young people? Gone! So it is always. We begin to moralise and look wise, and Beauty, who is something of a coquette, and of an exacting turn of mind, and likes attentions, gets disgusted with our wisdom or our stupidity, and goes off in a huff. Let the baggage go!

The ruined chapel adjoins the ruined castle on which I am now sitting, and is evidently a building of much older date. It is a mere shell now. It is quite roofless, ivy covers it in part; the stone tracery of the great western window is yet intact, but the coloured glass is gone with the splendid vestments of the abbot, the fuming incense, the chanting choirs, and the patient, sad-eyed monks, who muttered *Aves*, shrived guilt, and illuminated missals. Time was when this place breathed actual benedictions, and was a home of active peace. At present it is visited only by the stranger, and delights but the antiquary. The village people have so little respect for it, that they do not even consider it haunted. There are several tombs in the interior bearing knights' escutcheons, which time has sadly defaced. The dust you stand upon is noble. Earls have been brought here in dinted mail from battle, and earls' wives from the pangs of child-bearing. The last trumpet will break the slumber of a right honourable company. One of the tombs—the most perfect of all in point of preservation—I look at often, and try to conjecture what it commemorates. With all my fancies, I can get no further than the old story of love and death. There, on the slab, the white figures sleep; marble hands, folded in prayer, on marble breasts. And I like to think that he was brave, she beautiful; that although the monument is worn by time, and sullied by the stains of the weather, the qualities which it commemorates— husbandly and wifely affection, courtesy, courage, knightly scorn of wrong and falsehood, meekness, penitence, charity—are existing yet somewhere, recognisable by each other. The man who in this world can keep the whiteness of his soul, is not likely to lose it in any other.

In summer I spent a good deal of time floating about the lake. The landing-place to which my boat is tethered is ruinous, like the chapel and palace, and my embarkation causes quite a stir in the sleepy little village. Small boys leave their games and mud-pies, and gather round in silence;

they have seen me get off a hundred times, but
their interest in the matter seems always new.
Not unfrequently an idle cobbler, in red nightcap
and leathern apron, leans on a broken stile, and
honours my proceedings with his attention. I
shoot off, and the human knot dissolves. The
lake contains three islands, each with a solitary
tree, and on these islands the swans breed. I feed
the birds daily with bits of bread. See, one comes
gliding towards me, with superbly arched neck,
to receive its customary alms! How wildly beautiful its motions! How haughtily it begs! The green
pasture lands run down to the edge of the water,
and into it in the afternoons the red kine wade
and stand knee-deep in their shadows, surrounded
by troops of flies. Patiently the honest creatures
abide the attacks of their tormentors. Now one
swishes itself with its tail—now its neighbour
flaps a huge ear. I draw my oars alongside, and
let my boat float at its own will. The soft blue
heavenly abysses, the wandering streams of vapour, the long beaches of rippled cloud, are glassed
and repeated in the lake. Dreamthorp is silent as
a picture, the voices of the children are mute; and
the smoke from the houses, the blue pillars all
sloping in one angle, float upward as if in sleep.
Grave and stern the old castle rises from its
emerald banks, which long ago came down to the
lake in terrace on terrace, gay with fruits and
flowers, and with stone nymph and satyrs hid in
every nook. Silent and empty enough to-day! A

flock of daws suddenly bursts out from a turret, and round and round they wheel, as if in panic. Has some great scandal exploded? Has a conspiracy been discovered? Has a revolution broken out? The excitement has subsided, and one of them, perched on the old banner-staff, chatters confidentially to himself as he, sideways, eyes the world beneath him. Floating about thus, time passes swiftly, for, before I know where I am, the kine have withdrawn from the lake to couch on the herbage, while one on a little height is lowing for the milkmaid and her pails. Along the road I see the labourers coming home for supper, while the sun setting behind me makes the village windows blaze; and so I take out my oars, and pull leisurely through waters faintly flushed with evening colours.

I do not think that Mr. Buckle could have written his "History of Civilisation" in Dreamthorp, because in it books, conversation, and the other appurtenances of intellectual life, are not to be procured. I am acquainted with birds, and the building of nests—with wild-flowers, and the seasons in which they blow—but with the big world far away, with what men and women are thinking, and doing, and saying, I am acquainted only through the *Times*, and the occasional magazine or review, sent by friends whom I have not looked upon for years, but by whom, it seems, I am not yet forgotten. The village has but few intellectual wants, and the intellectual supply is strictly measured by the demand. Still there is something. Down in the village, and opposite the curiously-carved fountain, is a schoolroom which can accommodate a couple of hundred people on a pinch. There are our public meetings held. Musical entertainments have been given there by a single performer. In that schoolroom last winter an American biologist terrified the villagers, and, to their simple understandings, mingled up the next world with this. Now and again some rare bird of an itinerant lecturer covers dead walls with posters, yellow and blue, and to that schoolroom we flock to hear him. His rounded periods the eloquent gentleman devolves amidst a respectful silence. His audience do not understand him, but they see that the clergyman does, and the doctor does; and so they are content, and look as attentive and wise as possible. Then, in connexion with the schoolroom, there is a public library, where books are exchanged once a month. This library is a kind of Greenwich Hospital for disabled novels and romances. Each of these books has been in the wars; some are unquestionable antiques. The tears of three generations have fallen upon their dusky pages. The heroes and the heroines are of another age than ours. Sir Charles Grandison is standing with his hat under his arm. Tom Jones plops from the tree into the water, to the infinite distress of Sophia. Moses comes home from market with his stock of shagreen spectacles. Lovers, warriors, and villains—as dead to the present generation of readers as Cambyses—are weeping, fighting, and intriguing. These books, tattered and torn as they are, are read with delight to-day. The viands are celestial if set forth on a dingy tablecloth. The gaps and chasms which occur in pathetic or perilous chapters are felt to be personal calamities. It is with a certain feeling of tenderness that I look upon these books; I think of the dead fingers that have turned over the leaves, of the dead eyes that have travelled along the lines. An old novel has a history of its own. When fresh and new, and before it had breathed its secret, it lay on my lady's table. She killed the weary day with it, and when night came it was placed beneath her pillow. At the sea-side a couple of foolish heads have bent over it, hands have touched and tingled, and it has heard vows and protestations as passionate as any its pages contained. Coming down in the world, Cinderella in the kitchen has blubbered over it by the light of a surreptitious candle, conceiving herself the while the magnificent Georgiana, and Lord Mordaunt, Georgiana's lover, the pot-boy round the corner. Tied up with many a dingy brother, the auctioneer knocks the bundle down to the bidder of a few pence, and it finds its way to the quiet cove of some village library, where with some difficulty —as if from want of teeth, and with numerous interruptions—as if from lack of memory, it tells its old stories, and wakes tears, and blushes, and laughter as of yore. Thus it spends its age, and in a few years it will become unintelligible, and then, in the dust-bin, like poor human mortals in the grave, it will rest from all its labours. It is impossible to estimate the benefit which such books have conferred. How often have they loosed the chain of circumstance! What unfamiliar tears—what unfamiliar laughter they have caused! What chivalry and tenderness they have infused into rustic loves! Of what weary hours they have cheated and beguiled their readers! The big, solemn history-books are in excellent preservation; the story-books are defaced and frayed, and their out-of-elbows condition is their pride, and the best justification of their existence. They are tashed, as roses are, by being eagerly handled and smelt. I observe, too, that the most ancient romances are not in every case the most severely worn. It is the pace that tells in horses, men, and books. There are Nestors wonderfully hale; there are juveniles in a state of dilapidation. One of the youngest books, "The Old Curiosity Shop," is absolutely falling to pieces. That book, like Italy, is possessor of the fatal gift; but happily, in its case, everything can be rectified by a new edition. We have buried warriors and poets, princes and queens, but no one of these was followed to the grave by sincerer mourners than was little Nell.

Besides the itinerant lecturer, and the permanent library, we have the Sunday sermon.

These sum up the intellectual aids and further-
ances of the whole place. We have a church and
a chapel, and I attend both. The Dreamthorp
people are Dissenters, for the most part; why, I
never could understand; because dissent implies
a certain intellectual effort. But Dissenters they
are, and Dissenters they are likely to remain.
In an ungainly building, filled with hard gaunt
pews, without an organ, without a touch of colour
in the windows, with nothing to stir the imagination or the devotional sense, the simple people
worship. On Sunday, they are put upon a diet of
spiritual bread-and-water. Personally, I should
desire more generous food. But the labouring
people listen attentively, till once they fall asleep,
and they wake up to receive the benediction with
a feeling of having done their duty. They know
they ought to go to chapel, and they go. I go like-
wise, from habit, although I have long ago lost
the power of following a discourse. In my pew, and
whilst the clergyman is going on, I think of the
strangest things—of the tree at the window, of
the congregation of the dead outside, of the wheat-
fields and the corn-fields beyond and all around.
And the odd thing is, that it is during sermon
only that my mind flies off at a tangent and busies
itself with things removed from the place and the
circumstances. Whenever it is finished fancy re-
turns from her wanderings, and I am alive to the
objects around me. The clergyman knows my
humour, and is good Christian enough to forgive

me; and he smiles good-humouredly when I ask him to let me have the chapel keys, that I may enter, when in the mood, and preach a sermon to myself. To my mind, an empty chapel is impressive; a crowded one, comparatively a commonplace affair. Alone, I could choose my own text, and my silent discourse would not be without its practical applications.

An idle life I live in this place, as the world counts it; but then I have the satisfaction of differing from the world as to the meaning of idleness. A windmill twirling its arms all day is admirable only when there is corn to grind. Twirling its arms for the mere barren pleasure of twirling them, or for the sake of looking busy, does not deserve any rapturous paean of praise. I must be made happy after my own fashion, not after the fashion of other people. Here I can live as I please, here I can throw the reins on the neck of my whim. Here I play with my own thoughts; here I ripen for the grave.

ON THE WRITING OF ESSAYS

I HAVE already described my environments and my mode of life, and out of both I contrive to extract a very tolerable amount of satisfaction. Love in a cottage, with a broken window to let in the rain, is not my idea of comfort; no more is Dignity, walking forth richly clad, to whom every head uncovers, every knee grows supple. Bruin in winter-time fondly sucking his own paws, loses flesh; and love, feeding upon itself, dies of inanition. Take the candle of death in your hand, and walk through the stately galleries of the world, and their splendid furniture and array are as the tinsel armour and pasteboard goblets of a penny theatre; fame is but an inscription on a grave, and glory the melancholy blazon on a coffin-lid. We argue fiercely about happiness. One insists that she is found in the cottage which the hawthorn shades. Another that she is a lady of fashion, and treads on cloth of gold. Wisdom, listening to both, shakes a white head, and considers that "a good deal may be said on both sides."

There is a wise saying to the effect that "a man can eat no more than he can hold." Every man gets about the same satisfaction out of life. Mr. Suddlechops, the barber of Seven Dials, is as happy as Alexander at the head of his legions. The business of the one is to depopulate kingdoms, the business of the other to reap beards seven days old; but their relative positions do not affect the question. The one works with razors and soap-lather, the other with battle-cries and well-greaved Greeks. The one of a Saturday night counts up his shabby gains and grumbles; the other on *his* Saturday night sits down and weeps for other worlds to conquer. The pence to Mr. Suddlechops are as important as are the worlds to Alexander. Every condition of life has its peculiar advantages, and wisdom points these out and is contented with them. The varlet who sang—

> *A king cannot swagger*
> *Or get drunk like a beggar,*
> *Nor be half so happy as I—*

had the soul of a philosopher in him. The harshness of the parlour is revenged at night in the servants' hall. The coarse rich man rates his domestic, but there is a thought in the domestic's brain, docile and respectful as he looks, which makes the matter equal, which would madden the rich man if he knew it—make him wince as with a shrewdest twinge of hereditary gout. For insult and degradation are not without their peculiar solaces. You may spit upon Shylock's gaberdine, but the day comes when he demands his pound of flesh; every blow, every insult, not without a certain satisfaction, he adds to the account running up against you in the day-book and ledger of his hate—which at the proper time he will ask you to discharge. Every way we look we see even-handed nature administering her laws of compensation. Grandeur has a heavy tax to pay. The usurper rolls along like a god, surrounded by his guards. He dazzles the crowd—all very fine; but look beneath his splendid trappings and you see a shirt of mail, and beneath *that* a heart cowering in terror of an air-drawn dagger. Whom did the memory of Austerlitz most keenly sting? The beaten emperors? or the mighty Napoleon, dying like an untended watch-fire on St. Helena?

Giddy people may think the life I lead here staid and humdrum, but they are mistaken. It is true, I hear no concerts, save those in which the thrushes are performers in the spring mornings. I see no pictures, save those painted on the wide sky-canvas with the colours of sunrise and sunset. I attend neither rout nor ball; I have no deeper dissipation than the tea-table; I hear no more exciting scandal than quiet village gossip. Yet I enjoy my concerts more than I would the great London ones. I like the pictures I see, and think them better painted, too, than those which adorn the walls of the Royal Academy; and the

village gossip is more after my turn of mind than
the scandals that convulse the clubs. It is wonderful how the whole world reflects itself in the
simple village life. The people around me are full
of their own affairs and interests; were they of
imperial magnitude, they could not be excited
more strongly. Farmer Worthy is anxious about
the next market; the likelihood of a fall in the
price of butter and eggs hardly allows him to
sleep o' nights. The village doctor—happily we
have only one—skirrs hither and thither in his
gig, as if man could neither die nor be born without his assistance. He is continually standing on
the confines of existence, welcoming the new
comer, bidding farewell to the goer-away. And the
robustious fellow who sits at the head of the table
when the Jolly Swillers meet at the Blue Lion
on Wednesday evenings is a great politician,
sound of lung metal, and wields the village in the
taproom, as my Lord Palmerston wields the nation in the House. His listeners think him a wiser
personage than the Premier, and he is inclined to
lean to that opinion himself. I find everything
here that other men find in the big world. London
is but a magnified Dreamthorp.

And just as the Rev. Mr. White took note of
the ongoings of the seasons in and around Hamp-
shire Selborne, watched the colonies of the rooks
in the tall elms, looked after the swallows in the
cottage and rectory eaves, played the affectionate
spy on the private lives of chaffinch and hedge-

sparrow, was eavesdropper to the solitary cuckoo; so here I keep eye and ear open; take note of man, woman, and child; find many a pregnant text imbedded in the commonplace of village life; and, out of what I see and hear, weave in my own room my essays as solitarily as the spider weaves his web in the darkened corner. The essay, as a literary form, resembles the lyric, in so far as it is moulded by some central mood—whimsical, serious, or satirical. Give the mood, and the essay, from the first sentence to the last, grows around it as the cocoon grows around the silkworm. The essay-writer is a chartered libertine, and a law unto himself. A quick ear and eye, an ability to discern the infinite suggestiveness of common things, a brooding meditative spirit, are all that the essayist requires to start business with. Jacques, in "As You Like It," had the makings of a charming essayist. It is not the essayist's duty to inform, to build pathways through metaphysical morasses, to cancel abuses, any more than it is the duty of the poet to do these things. Incidentally he may do something in that way, just as the poet may, but it is not his duty, and should not be expected of him. Skylarks are primarily created to sing, although a whole choir of them may be baked in pies and brought to table; they were born to make music, although they may incidentally stay the pangs of vulgar hunger. The essayist is a kind of poet in prose, and if questioned harshly as to his uses, he might be unable to render a better apology for his existence than a flower might. The essay should be pure literature as the poem is pure literature. The essayist wears a lance, but he cares more for the sharpness of its point than for the pennon that flutters on it, than for the banner of the captain under whom he serves. He plays with death as Hamlet plays with Yorick's skull, and he reads the morals—strangely stern, often, for such fragrant lodging—which are folded up in the bosoms of roses. He has no pride, and is deficient in a sense of the congruity and fitness of things. He lifts a pebble from the ground, and puts it aside more carefully than any gem; and on a nail in a cottage-door he will hang the mantle of his thought, heavily brocaded with the gold of rhetoric. He finds his way into the Elysian fields through portals the most shabby and commonplace.

The essayist plays with his subject, now in whimsical, now in grave, now in melancholy mood. He lies upon the idle grassy bank, like Jacques, letting the world flow past him, and from this thing and the other he extracts his mirth and his moralities. His main gift is an eye to discover the suggestiveness of common things; to find a sermon in the most unpromising texts. Beyond the vital hint, the first step, his discourses are not beholden to their titles. Let him take up the most trivial subject, and it will lead him away to the great questions over which the serious imagination loves to brood—fortune, mutability, death —just as inevitably as the runnel, trickling among the summer hills, on which sheep are bleating, leads you to the sea; or as, turning down the first street you come to in the city, you are led finally, albeit by many an intricacy, out into the open country, with its waste places and its woods, where you are lost in a sense of strangeness and solitariness. The world is to the meditative man what the mulberry plant is to the silkworm. The essay-writer has no lack of subject-matter. He has the day that is passing over his head; and, if unsatisfied with that, he has the world's six thousand years to depasture his gay or serious humour upon. I idle away my time here, and I am finding new subjects every hour. Everything I see or hear is an essay in bud. The world is everywhere whispering essays, and one need only be the world's amanuensis. The proverbial expression which last evening the clown dropped as he trudged homeward to supper, the light of the setting sun on his face, expands before me to a dozen pages. The coffin of the pauper, which to-day I saw carried carelessly along, is as good a subject as the funeral procession of an emperor. Craped drum and banner add nothing to death; penury and disrespect take nothing away. Incontinently my thought moves like a slow-paved hearse with sable nodding plumes. Two rustic lovers, whispering between the darkening hedges, is as potent to project my mind into the tender passion as if I had seen Romeo touch the cheek of Juliet in the moonlight garden. Seeing a curly-headed child asleep in the sunshine before a cottage-door is sufficient excuse for a discourse on childhood; quite as good as if I had seen infant Cain asleep in the lap of Eve with Adam looking on. A lark cannot rise to heaven without raising as many thoughts as there are notes in its song. Dawn cannot pour its white light on my village without starting from their dim lair a hundred reminiscences; nor can sunset burn above yonder trees in the west without attracting to itself the melancholy of a lifetime. When spring unfolds her green leaves I would be provoked to indite an essay on hope and youth, were it not that it is already writ in the carols of the birds; and I might be tempted in autumn to improve the occasion, were it not for the rustle of the withered leaves as I walk through the woods. Compared with that simple music, the saddest-cadenced words have but a shallow meaning.

The essayist who feeds his thoughts upon the segment of the world which surrounds him cannot avoid being an egotist; but then his egotism is not unpleasing. If he be without taint of boastfulness, of self-sufficiency, of hungry vanity, the world will not press the charge home. If a man discourses continually of his wines, his plate, his titled acquaintances, the number and quality of his horses, his men-servants and maid-servants, he must discourse very skilfully indeed if he escapes being called a coxcomb. If a man speaks of death—tells you that the idea of it continually haunts him, that he has the most insatiable curiosity as to death and dying, that his thought mines in churchyards like a "demon-mole"—no one is specially offended, and that this is a dull fellow is the hardest thing likely to be said of him. Only, the egotism that over-crows you is offensive, that exalts trifles and takes pleasure in them, that suggests superiority in matters of equipage and furniture; and the egotism is offensive, because it runs counter to and jostles your self-complacency. The egotism which rises no higher than the grave is of a solitary and a hermit kind—it crosses no man's path, it disturbs no man's *amour propre*. You may offend a man if you say you are as rich as he, as wise as he, as handsome as he. You offend no man if you tell him that, like him, you have to die. The king, in his crown and coronation robes, will allow the beggar to claim that relationship with him. To have to die is a distinction of which no man is proud. The speaking about one's self is not necessarily offensive. A modest, truthful man speaks better about himself than about anything else, and on that subject his speech is likely to be most profitable to his hearers. Certainly, there is no subject with which he is better acquainted, and on which he has a better title to be heard. And it is this egotism, this perpetual reference to self, in which the charm of the essayist resides. If a man is worth knowing at all,

he is worth knowing well. The essayist gives you
his thoughts, and lets you know, in addition, how
he came by them. He has nothing to conceal; he
throws open his doors and windows, and lets him
enter who will. You like to walk round peculiar
or important men as you like to walk round a
building, to view it from different points, and in
different lights. Of the essayist, when his mood
is communicative, you obtain a full picture.
You are made his contemporary and familiar
friend. You enter into his humours and his seriousness. You are made heir of his whims, prejudices,
and playfulness. You walk through the whole
nature of him, as you walk through the streets
of Pompeii, looking into the interior of stately
mansions, reading the satirical scribblings on the
walls. And the essayist's habit of not only giving
you his thoughts, but telling you how he came by
them, is interesting, because it shews you by what
alchemy the ruder world becomes transmuted into
the finer. We like to know the lineage of ideas,
just as we like to know the lineage of great earls
and swift race-horses. We like to know that the
discovery of the law of gravitation was born of
the fall of an apple in an English garden on a
summer afternoon. Essays written after this fashion are racy of the soil in which they grow, as
you taste the lava in the vines grown on the slopes
of Etna, they say. There is a healthy Gascon flavour in Montaigne's Essays; and Charles Lamb's
are scented with the primroses of Covent Garden.

ON THE WRITING OF ESSAYS

The essayist does not usually appear early in the literary history of a country: he comes naturally after the poet and the chronicler. His habit of mind is leisurely; he does not write from any special stress of passionate impulse; he does not create material so much as he comments upon material already existing. It is essential for him that books should have been written, and that they should, at least to some extent, have been read and digested. He is usually full of allusions and references, and these his reader must be able to follow and understand. And in this literary walk, as in most others, the giants came first: Montaigne and Lord Bacon were our earliest essayists, and, as yet, they are our best. In point of style, these essays are different from anything that could now be produced. Not only is the thinking different—the manner of setting forth the thinking is different also. We despair of reaching the thought, we despair equally of reaching the language. We can no more bring back their turns of sentence than we can bring back their tournaments. Montaigne, in his serious moods, has a curiously rich and intricate eloquence; and Bacon's sentence bends beneath the weight of his thought, like a branch beneath the weight of its fruit. Bacon seems to have written his essays with Shakspeare's pen. There is a certain want of ease about the old writers which has an irresistible charm. The language flows like a stream over a pebbled bed, with propulsion, eddy, and sweet recoil—the pebbles, if retarding movement, giving ring and dimple to the surface, and breaking the whole into babbling music. There is a ceremoniousness in the mental habits of these ancients. Their intellectual garniture is picturesque, like the garniture of their bodies. Their thoughts are courtly and high mannered. A singular analogy exists between the personal attire of a period and its written style. The peaked beard, the starched collar, the quilted doublet, have their correspondences in the high sentence and elaborate ornament (worked upon the thought like figures upon tapestry) of Sidney and Spenser. In Pope's day men wore rapiers, and their weapons they carried with them into literature, and frequently unsheathed them too. They knew how to stab to the heart with an epigram. Style went out with the men who wore knee-breeches and buckles in their shoes. We write more easily now; but in our easy writing there is ever a taint of flippancy: our writing is to theirs, what shooting-coat and wideawake are to doublet and plumed hat.

Montaigne and Bacon are our earliest and greatest essayists, and likeness and unlikeness exist between the men. Bacon was constitutionally the graver nature. He writes like one on whom presses the weight of affairs, and he approaches a subject always on its serious side. He does not play with it fantastically. He lives amongst great ideas, as with great nobles, with whom he dare not be too familiar. In the tone of his mind there is ever something imperial. When he writes on building, he speaks of a palace with spacious entrances, and courts, and banqueting-halls; when he writes on gardens, he speaks of alleys and mounts, waste places and fountains, of a garden "which is indeed prince-like." To read over his table of contents, is like reading over a roll of peers' names. We have, taking them as they stand, essays treating *Of Great Place, Of Boldness, Of Goodness, and Goodness of Nature, Of Nobility, Of Seditions and Troubles, Of Atheism, Of Superstition, Of Travel, Of Empire, Of Counsel,*—a book plainly to lie in the closets of statesmen and princes, and designed to nurture the noblest natures. Bacon always seems to write with his ermine on. Montaigne was different from all this. His table of contents reads in comparison like a medley, or a catalogue of an auction. He was quite as wise as Bacon; he could look through men quite as clearly, and search them quite as narrowly; certain of his moods were quite as serious, and in one corner of his heart he kept a yet profounder melancholy; but he was volatile, a humorist, and a gossip. He could be dignified enough on great occasions, but dignity and great occasions bored him. He could stand in the presence with propriety enough, but then he got out of the presence as rapidly as possible. When, in the thirty-eighth year of his age, he—somewhat world-weary, and with more scars on his heart than he cared to discover—retired to his château, he placed his library "in the great tower over-looking the entrance to the court," and over the central rafter he inscribed in large letters the de-vice—"I DO NOT UNDERSTAND; I PAUSE; I EX-AMINE." When he began to write his Essays he had no great desire to shine as an author; he wrote simply to relieve teeming heart and brain. The best method to lay the spectres of the mind is to commit them to paper. Speaking of the Es-says, he says, "This book has a domestic and private object. It is intended for the use of my relations and friends; so that, when they have lost me, which they will soon do, they may find in it some features of my condition and humours; and by this means keep up more completely, and in a more lively manner, the knowledge they have of me." In his Essays he meant to portray himself, his habits, his modes of thought, his opinions, what fruit of wisdom he had gathered from experience sweet and bitter; and the task he has executed with wonderful fidelity. He does not make himself a hero. Cromwell would have his warts painted; and Montaigne paints his, and paints them too with a certain fondness. He is perfectly tolerant of himself and of everybody else. Whatever be the subject, the writing flows on easy, equable, self-satisfied, almost always with a personal anecdote floating on the surface. Each event of his past life he considers a fact of nature; creditable or the reverse, there it is; some-times to be speculated upon, not in the least to be regretted. If it is worth nothing else, it may be made the subject of an essay, or, at least, be useful as an illustration. We have not only his thoughts, we see also how and from what they arose. When he presents you with a bouquet, you notice that the flowers have been plucked up by the roots, and to the roots a portion of the soil still adheres. On his daily life his Essays grew like lichens upon rocks. If a thing is useful to him, he is not squeamish as to where he picks it up. In his eyes there is nothing common or unclean; and he accepts a favour as willingly from a beggar as from a prince. When it serves his purpose, he quotes a tavern catch, or the smart saying of a kitchen wench, with as much relish as the fine sentiment of a classical poet, or the gallant *bon mot* of a king. Everything is important which relates to himself. That his moustache, if stroked with his perfumed glove, or handkerchief, will retain the odour a whole day, is related with as much gravity as the loss of a battle, or the march of a desolating plague. Montaigne, in his grave passages, reaches an eloquence intricate and highly wrought; but then his moods are Protean, and he is constantly alternating his stateliness with familiarity, anecdote, humour, coarseness. His Essays are like a mythological landscape—you hear the pipe of Pan in the distance, the naked goddess moves past, the satyr leers from the thicket. At the core of him profoundly melancholy, and consumed by a hunger for truth, he stands like Prospero in the enchanted island, and he has Ariel and Caliban to do his behests and run his errands. Sudden alternations are very characteristic of him. Whatever he says suggests its opposite. He laughs at himself and his reader. He builds his castle of cards for the mere pleasure of knocking it down again. He is ever unexpected and surprising. And with this curious mental activity, this play and linked dance of discordant elements, his page is alive and restless, like the constant flicker of light and shadow in a mass of foliage which the wind is stirring.

Montaigne is avowedly an egotist; and by those who are inclined to make this a matter of reproach, it should be remembered that the value of egotism depends entirely on the egotist. If the egotist is weak, his egotism is worthless. If the egotist is strong, acute, full of distinctive character, his egotism is precious, and remains a possession of the race. If Shakspeare had left personal revelations, how we should value them; if, indeed, he has not in some sense left them—if the tragedies and comedies are not personal revelations altogether—the multiform nature of the man rushing toward the sun at once in Falstaff, Hamlet, and Romeo. But calling Montaigne an egotist does not go a great way to decipher him. No writer takes the reader so much into his confidence, and no one so entirely escapes the penalty of confidence. He tells us everything about himself, we think; and when all is told, it is astonishing how little we really know. The esplanades of Montaigne's palace are thoroughfares, men from every European country rub clothes there, but somewhere in the building there is a secret room in which the master sits, of which no one but himself wears the key. We read in the Essays about his wife, his daughter, his daughter's governess, of his cook, of his page, "who was never found guilty of telling the truth," of his library, the Gascon harvest outside his château, his habits of composition, his favourite speculations; but somehow the man himself is constantly eluding us. His daughter's governess, his page, the ripening Gascon fields, are never introduced for their own sakes; they are employed to illustrate and set off the subject on which he happens to be writing. A brawl in his own kitchen he does not consider worthy of being specially set down, but he has seen and heard everything; it comes in his way when travelling in some remote region, and accordingly it finds a place. He is the frankest, most outspoken of writers; and that very frankness and outspokenness puts the reader off his guard. If you wish to preserve your secret, wrap it up in frankness. The Essays are full of this trick. The frankness is as well simulated as the grape-branches of the Grecian artist which the birds flew towards and pecked. When Montaigne retreats, he does so like a skilful general, leaving his fires burning. In other ways, too, he is an adept in putting his reader out. He discourses with the

utmost gravity, but you suspect mockery or banter in his tones. He is serious with the most trifling
subjects, and he trifles with the most serious.
"He broods eternally over his own thought," but
who can tell what his thought may be for the
nonce? He is of all writers the most vagrant, surprising, and, to many minds, illogical. His sequences are not the sequences of other men. His
writings are as full of transformations as a pantomime or a fairy tale. His arid wastes lead up
to glittering palaces, his banqueting-halls end in
a dog-hutch. He begins an essay about trivialities,
and the conclusion is in the other world. And the
peculiar character of his writing, like the peculiar
character of all writing which is worth anything,
arises from constitutional turn of mind. He is
constantly playing at fast and loose with himself
and his reader. He mocks and scorns his deeper
nature; and, like Shakspeare in Hamlet, says his
deepest things in a jesting way. When he is
gayest, be sure there is a serious design in his
gaiety. Singularly shrewd and penetrating—sad,
not only from sensibility of exquisite nerve and
tissue, but from meditation, and an eye that
pierced the surfaces of things—fond of pleasure,
yet strangely fascinated by death—sceptical, yet
clinging to what the Church taught and believed
—lazily possessed by a high ideal of life, yet unable to reach it, careless perhaps often to strive
after it, and with no very high opinion of his own
goodness, or of the goodness of his fellows—and

with all these serious elements, an element of humour mobile as flame, which assumed a variety of forms, now pure fun, now mischievous banter, now blistering scorn—humour in all its shapes, carelessly exercised on himself and his readers— with all this variety, complexity, riot, and contradiction almost of intellectual forces within, Montaigne wrote his bewildering Essays—with the exception of Rabelais, the greatest modern Frenchman—the creator of a distinct literary form, and to whom, down even to our own day, even in point of subject-matter, every essayist has been more or less indebted.

Bacon is the greatest of the serious and stately essayists—Montaigne the greatest of the garrulous and communicative. The one gives you his thoughts on Death, Travel, Government, and the like, and lets you make the best of them; the other gives you his on the same subjects, but he wraps them up in personal gossip and reminiscence. With the last it is never Death or Travel alone; it is always Death one-fourth, and Montaigne three-fourths; or Travel one-fourth, and Montaigne three-fourths. He pours his thought into the water of gossip, and gives you to drink. He gilds his pill always, and he always gilds it with himself. The general characteristics of his Essays have been indicated, and it is worth while inquiring what they teach, what positive good they have done, and why for three centuries they have charmed, and still continue to charm.

The Essays contain a philosophy of life, which is not specially high, yet which is certain to find acceptance more or less with men who have passed out beyond the glow of youth, and who have made trial of the actual world. The essence of his philosophy is a kind of cynical common sense. He will risk nothing in life; he will keep to the beaten track; he will not let passion blind or enslave him; he will gather around him what good he can, and will therewith endeavour to be content. He will be, as far as possible, self-sustained; he will not risk his happiness in the hands of man, or of woman either. He is shy of friendship, he fears love, for he knows that both are dangerous. He knows that life is full of bitters, and he holds it wisdom that a man should console himself, as far as possible, with its sweets, the principal of which are peace, travel, leisure, and the writing of essays. He values obtainable Gascon bread and cheese more than the unobtainable stars. He thinks crying for the moon the foolishest thing in the world. He will remain where he is. He will not deny that a new world may exist beyond the sunset, but he knows that to reach the new world there is a troublesome Atlantic to cross; and he is not in the least certain that, putting aside the chance of being drowned on the way, he will be one whit happier in the new world than he is in the old. For his part he will embark with no Columbus. He feels that life is but a sad thing at best; but as he has little hope of making it better, he accepts it, and will not make it worse by murmuring. When the chain galls him, he can at least revenge himself by making jests on it. He will temper the despotism of nature by epigrams. He has read Aesop's fable, and is the last man in the world to relinquish the shabbiest substance to grasp at the finest shadow.

Of nothing under the sun was Montaigne quite certain, except that every man—whatever his station—might travel farther and fare worse; and that the playing with his own thoughts, in the shape of essay-writing, was the most harmless of amusements. His practical acquiescence in things does not promise much fruit, save to himself; yet in virtue of it he became one of the forces of the world—a very visible agent in bringing about the Europe which surrounds us to-day. He lived in the midst of the French religious wars. The rulers of his country were execrable Christians, but most orthodox Catholics. The burning of heretics was a public amusement, and the court ladies sat out the play. On the queen-mother and on her miserable son lay all the blood of the St. Bartholomew. The country was torn asunder; everywhere was battle, murder, pillage, and such woeful partings as Mr. Millais has represented in his incomparable picture. To the solitary humorous essayist this state of things was hateful. He was a good Catholic in his easy way; he attended divine service regularly; he crossed himself when he yawned. He conformed in practice to every rule of the Church; but if orthodox in these matters, he was daring in speculation. There was nothing he was not bold enough to question. He waged war after his peculiar fashion with every form of superstition. He worked under the foundations of priestcraft. But while serving the Reformed cause, he had no sympathy with Reformers. If they would but remain quiet, but keep their peculiar notions to themselves, France would rest! That a man should go to the stake for an opinion, was as incomprehensible to him as that a priest or king should send him there for an opinion. He thought the persecuted and the persecutors fools about equally matched. He was easy-tempered and humane—in the hunting-field, he could not bear the cry of a dying hare with composure—martyr-burning had consequently no attraction for such a man. His scepticism came into play, his melancholy humour, his sense of the illimitable which surrounds man's life, and which mocks, defeats, flings back his thought upon himself. Man is here, he said, with bounded powers, with limited knowledge, with an unknown behind, an unknown in front, assured of nothing but that he was born, and that he must die; why, then, in Heaven's name should he burn his fellow for a difference of opinion in the matter of surplices, or as to the proper fashion of conducting devotion? Out of his scepticism and his merciful disposition grew, in that fiercely intolerant age, the idea of toleration, of which he was the apostle.

Widely read, charming every one by his wit and wisdom, his influence spread from mind to mind, and assisted in bringing about the change which has taken place in European thought. His ideas, perhaps, did not spring from the highest sources, He was no ascetic, he loved pleasure, he was tolerant of everything except cruelty; but on that account we should not grudge him his meed. It is in this indirect way that great writers take their place among the forces of the world. In the long run, genius and wit side with the right cause. And the man fighting against wrong to-day is assisted, in a greater degree than perhaps he is himself aware, by the sarcasm of this writer, the metaphor of that, the song of the other, although the writers themselves professed indifference, or were even counted as belonging to the enemy.

Montaigne's hold on his readers arises from many causes. There is his frank and curious self-delineation; *that* interests, because it is the revelation of a very peculiar nature. Then there is the positive value of separate thoughts imbedded in his strange whimsicality and humour. Lastly, there is the perennial charm of style, which is never a separate quality, but rather the amalgam and issue of all the mental and moral qualities in a man's possession, and which bears the same relation to these that light bears to the mingled elements that make up the orb of the sun. And style, after all, rather than thought, is the immortal thing in literature. In literature, the charm

of style is indefinable, yet all-subduing, just as
fine manners are in social life. In reality, it is not
of so much consequence what you say, as how you
say it. Memorable sentences are memorable on
account of some single irradiating word. "But
Shadwell never *deviates* into sense, for instance."
Young Roscius, in his provincial barn, will repeat
you the great soliloquy of Hamlet, and although
every word may be given with tolerable correct-
ness, you find it just as commonplace as himself;
the great actor speaks it, and you "read Shakspeare as by a flash of lightning." And it is in
Montaigne's style, in the strange freaks and turn-
ings of his thought, his constant surprises, his
curious alternations of humour and melancholy,
his careless, familiar form of address, and the grace
with which everything is done, that his charm lies,
and which makes the hundredth perusal of him
as pleasant as the first.

And on style depends the success of the essayist.
Montaigne said the most familiar things in the
finest way. Goldsmith could not be termed a
thinker; but everything he touched he brightened,
as after a month of dry weather, the shower
brightens the dusty shrubbery of a suburban villa.
The world is not so much in need of new thoughts
as that when thought grows old and worn with
usage it should, like current coin, be called in,
and, from the mint of genius, reissued fresh and
new. Love is an old story enough, but in every
generation it is re-born, in the downcast eyes and

blushes of young maidens. And so, although he fluttered in Eden, Cupid is young to-day. If Montaigne had lived in Dreamthorp, as I am now living, had he written essays as I am now writing them, his English Essays would have been as good as his Gascon ones. Looking on, the country cart would not for nothing have passed him on the road to market, the setting sun would be arrested in its splendid colours, the idle chimes of the church would be translated into a thoughtful music. As it is, the village life goes on, and there is no result. My sentences are not much more brilliant than the speeches of the clowns; in my book there is little more life than there is in the market-place on the days when there is no market.

ON DEATH AND THE FEAR OF DYING

LET me curiously analyse eternal farewells, and the last pressures of loving hands. Let me smile at faces bewept, and the nodding plumes and slow paces of funerals. Let me write down brave heroical sentences—sentences that defy death, as brazen Goliath the hosts of Israel.

"When death waits for us is uncertain; let us everywhere look for him. The premeditation of death is the premeditation of liberty; who has learnt to die, has forgot to serve. There is nothing of evil in life for him who rightly comprehends that death is no evil; to know how to die delivers us from all subjection and constraint. *Paulus Æmilius* answered him whom the miserable *king of Macedon*, his prisoner, sent to entreat him that he would not lead him in his triumph, '*Let him make that request to himself.*' In truth, in all things, if nature do not help a little, it is very hard for art and industry to perform anything to purpose. I am, in my own nature, not melancholy, but thoughtful; and there is nothing I have more continually entertained myself withal than the imaginations of death, even in the gayest and most wanton time of my age. In the company of ladies, and in the height of mirth, some have perhaps thought me possessed of some jealousy, or meditating upon the uncertainty of some imagined hope, whilst I was entertaining myself with the remembrance of some one surprised a few days before with a burning fever, of which he died, returning from an entertainment like this, with his head full of idle fancies of love and jollity, as mine was then; and for aught I knew, the same destiny was attending me. Yet did not this thought wrinkle my forehead any more than any other." . . . "Why dost thou fear this last day? It contributes no more to thy destruction than every one of the rest. The last step is not the cause of lassitude, it does but confer it. Every day travels toward death; the last only arrives at it. These are the good lessons our mother nature teaches. I have often considered with myself whence it should proceed, that in war the image of death— whether we look upon it as to our own particular danger, or that of another—should, without comparison, appear less dreadful than at home in our own houses (for if it were not so, it would be an army of whining milksops), and that being still in all places the same, there should be, notwithstanding, much more assurance in peasants and the meaner sort of people, than others of better quality and education; and I do verily believe, that it is those terrible ceremonies and preparations wherewith we set it out, that more terrify us than the thing itself; a new, quite contrary way of living, the cries of mothers, wives, and children, the visits of astonished and affected friends, the attendance of pale and blubbered servants, a dark room set round with burning tapers, our beds environed with physicians and divines; in fine, nothing but ghostliness and horror round about us, render it so formidable, that a man almost fancies himself dead and buried already. Children are afraid even of those they love best, and are best acquainted with, when disguised in a vizor, and so are we; the vizor must be removed as well from things as persons; which being taken away, we shall find nothing underneath but the very same death that a mean servant, or a poor chambermaid, died a day or two ago, without any manner of apprehension or concern."[1]

"Men feare *death* as children feare to goe in the darke; and as that natural feare in children is increased with tales, so in the other. Certainly the contemplation of *death* as the *wages of sinne*, and passage to another world, is holy and religious; but the feare of it as a tribute due unto nature, is weake. Yet in religious meditations there is sometimes mixture of vanitie and of superstition. You shal reade in some of the friars' books of *mortification*, that a man should thinke unto himself what the paine is if he have but his finger-end pressed or tortured; and thereby imagine what

[1]Montaigne.

the paines of *death* are when the whole body is corrupted and dissolved; when many times *death* passeth with lesse paine than the torture of a Lemme. For the most vitall parts are not the quickest of sense. Groanes and convulsions, and a discoloured face, and friends weeping, and blackes and obsequies, and the like, shew *death* terrible. It is worthy the observing, that there is no passion in the minde of man so weake but it mates and masters the feare of *death;* and therefore death is no such terrible enemy when a man hath so many attendants about him that can winne the combat of him. *Revenge* triumphs over *death, love* subjects it, *honour* aspireth to it, *griefe* fleeth to it, *feare* pre-occupieth it; nay, we read, after *Otho* the emperour had slaine himselfe, *pitty,* (which is the tenderest of affections,) provoked many to die, out of meer compassion to their soveraigne, and as the truest sort of followers. . . . It is as naturall to die as to be borne; and to a little infant, perhaps, the one is as painfull as the other. He that dies in an earnest pursuit is like one that is wounded in hot blood, who for the time scarce feels the hurt; and, therefore, a minde fixt and bent upon somewhat that is good, doth avert the sadness of *death*. But above all, believe it, the sweetest canticle is, *Nunc Dimittis,* when a man hath obtained worthy ends and expectations. Death hath this also; that it openeth the gate to good fame, and extinguisheth envie."[1]

[1]Bacon.

These sentences of the great essayists are brave
and ineffectual as Leonidas and his Greeks. Death
cares very little for sarcasm or trope; hurl at him
a javelin or a rose, it is all one. We build around
ourselves ramparts of stoical maxims, edifying
to witness, but when the terror comes these yield
as the knots of river flags to the shoulder of
Behemoth.

Death is terrible only in presence. When distant, or supposed to be distant, we can call him
hard or tender names, nay, even poke our poor
fun at him. *Mr. Punch*, on one occasion, when he
wished to ridicule the useful-information leanings
of a certain periodical publication, quoted from
its pages the sentences, "Man is mortal," and
people were found to grin broadly over the exquisite stroke of humour. Certainly the words,
and the fact they contain, are trite enough. Utter
the sentence gravely in any company, and you
are certain to provoke laughter. And yet some
subtle recognition of the fact of death runs constantly through the warp and woof of the most
ordinary human existence. And this recognition
does not always terrify. The spectre has the most
cunning disguises, and often when near us we are
unaware of the fact of proximity. Unsuspected,
this idea of death lurks in the sweetness of music;
it has something to do with the pleasure with
which we behold the vapours of morning; it
comes between the passionate lips of lovers; it
lives in the thrill of kisses. "An inch deeper,

and you will find the emperor." Probe joy to its last fibre, and you will find death. And it is the most merciful of all the merciful provisions of nature, that a haunting sense of insecurity should deepen the enjoyment of what we have secured; that the pleasure of our warm human day and its activities should to some extent arise from a vague consciousness of the waste night which environs it, in which no arm is raised, in which no voice is ever heard. Death is the ugly fact which nature has to hide, and she hides it well. Human life were otherwise an impossibility. The pantomime runs on merrily enough; but when once Harlequin lifts his vizor, Columbine disappears, the jest is frozen on the Clown's lips, and the hand of the filching Pantaloon is arrested in the act. Wherever death looks, *there* is silence and trembling. But although on every man he will one day or another look, he is coy of revealing himself till the appointed time. He makes his approaches like an Indian warrior, under covers and ambushes. We have our parts to play, and he remains hooded till they are played out. We are agitated by our passions, we busily pursue our ambitions, we are acquiring money or reputation, and all at once, in the centre of our desires, we discover the "Shadow feared of man." And so nature fools the poor human mortal evermore. When she means to be deadly, she dresses her face in smiles; when she selects a victim, she sends him a poisoned rose. There is no pleasure, no shape of good fortune, no form of glory in which death has not hid himself, and waited silently for his prey.

And death is the most ordinary thing in the world. It is as common as births; it is of more frequent occurrence than marriages and the attainment of majorities. But the difference between death and other forms of human experience lies in this, that we can gain no information about it. The dead man is wise, but he is silent. We cannot wring his secret from him. We cannot interpret the ineffable calm which gathers on the rigid face. As a consequence, when our thought rests on death we are smitten with isolation and loneliness. We are without company on the dark road; and we have advanced so far upon it that we cannot hear the voices of our friends. It is in this sense of loneliness, this consciousness of identity and nothing more, that the terror of dying consists. And yet, compared to that road, the most populous thoroughfare of London or Pekin is a desert. What enumerator will take for us the census of the dead? And this matter of death and dying, like most things else in the world, may be exaggerated by our own fears and hopes. Death, terrible to look forward to, may be pleasant even to look back at. Could we be admitted to the happy fields, and hear the conversations which blessed spirits hold, one might discover that to conquer death a man has but to die; that by that act terror is softened into familiarity, and that the remembrance of death becomes but as the remembrance of yesterday. To these fortunate ones death may be but a date, and dying a subject fruitful in comparisons, a matter on which experiences may be serenely compared. Meantime, however, *we* have not yet reached that measureless content, and death scares, piques, tantalises, as mind and nerve are built. Situated as we are, knowing that it is inevitable, we cannot keep our thoughts from resting on it curiously, at times. Nothing interests us so much. The Highland seer pretended that he could see the winding-sheet high upon the breast of the man for whom death was waiting. Could we behold any such visible sign, the man who bore it, no matter where he stood—even if he were a slave watching Cæsar pass—would usurp every eye. At the coronation of a king, the wearing of *that* order would dim royal robe, quench the sparkle of the diadem, and turn to vanity the herald's cry. Death makes the meanest beggar august, and that augustness would assert itself in the presence of a king. And it is this curiosity with regard to everything related to death and dying which makes us treasure up the last sayings of great men, and attempt to wring out of them tangible meanings. Was Goethe's "Light—light, more light!" a prayer, or a statement of spiritual experience, or simply an utterance of the fact that the room in which he lay was filling with the last twilight? In consonance with our own natures we interpret it the one way or the other—*he* is beyond our questioning. For the same reason it is that men take interest in executions—from Charles I on the scaffold at Whitehall, to Porteous in the Grassmarket execrated by the mob. These men are not dulled by disease, they are not delirious with fever; they look death in the face, and what in these circumstances they say and do has the strangest fascination for us.

What does the murderer think when his eyes are for ever blinded by the accursed nightcap? In what form did thought condense itself between the gleam of the lifted axe and the rolling of King Charles's head in the sawdust? This kind of speculation may be morbid, but it is not necessarily so. All extremes of human experience touch us; and we have all the deepest personal interest in the experience of death. Out of all we know about dying we strive to clutch something which may break its solitariness, and relieve us by a touch of companionship.

To denude death of its terrible associations were a vain attempt. The atmosphere is always cold around an iceberg. In the contemplation of dying the spirit may not flinch, but pulse and heart, colour and articulation, are always cowards. No philosophy will teach them bravery in the stern presence. And yet there are considerations which rob death of its ghastliness, and help to reconcile us to it. The thoughtful happiness of a human being is complex, and in certain moved moments, which, after they have gone, we can recognise to have been our happiest, some subtle thought of death has been curiously intermixed. And this subtle intermixture it is which gives the happy moment its character—which makes the difference between the gladness of a child, resident in mere animal health and impulse, and too volatile to be remembered, and the serious joy of a man, which looks before and after, and takes in both this world and the next. Speaking broadly, it may be said that it is from some obscure recognition of the fact of death that life draws its final sweetness. An obscure, haunting recognition, of course; for if more than that, if the thought becomes palpable, defined, and present, it swallows up everything. The howling of the winter wind outside increases the warm satisfaction of a man in bed; but this satisfaction is succeeded by quite another feeling when the wind grows into a tempest, and threatens to blow the house down. And this remote recognition of death may exist almost constantly in a man's mind, and give to his life keener zest and relish. His lights may burn the brighter for it, and his wines taste sweeter. For it is on the tapestry of a dim ground that the figures come out in the boldest relief and the brightest colour.

If we were to live here always, with no other care than how to feed, clothe, and house ourselves, life would be a very sorry business. It is immeasurably heightened by the solemnity of death. The brutes die even as we; but it is our knowledge that we have to die which makes us human. If nature cunningly hides death, and so permits us to play out our little games, it is easily seen that our knowing it to be inevitable, that to every one of us it will come one day or another, is a wonderful spur to action. We really do work while it is called today, because the night cometh when no man can work. We may not expect it soon—it may not have sent us a single *avant-courier*—yet we all know that every day brings it nearer. On the supposition that we were to live here always, there would be little inducement to exertion. But, having some work at heart, the knowledge that we may be, any day, finally interrupted, is an incentive to diligence. We naturally desire to have it completed, or at least far advanced toward completion, before that final interruption takes place. And knowing that his existence here is limited, a man's workings have reference to others rather than to himself, and thereby into his nature comes a new influx of nobility. If a man plants a tree, he knows that other hands than his will gather the fruit; and when he plants it, he thinks quite as much of those other hands as of his own. Thus to the poet there is the dearer life after life; and posterity's single laurel leaf is valued more than a multitude of contemporary bays. Even the man immersed in money-making does not make money so much for himself as for those who may come after him. Riches in noble natures have a double sweetness. The possessor enjoys his wealth, and he heightens that enjoyment by an imaginative entrance into the pleasure which his son or his nephew may derive from it when he is away, or the high uses to which he may turn it. Seeing that we have no perpetual lease of life and its adjuncts, we do not live for ourselves. And thus it is that death, which we are accustomed to consider an evil, really acts for us the friendliest part, and takes away the commonplace of existence. My life, and your life, flowing on thus day by day, is a vapid enough piece of business; but when we think that it must *close*, a multitude of considerations, not connected with ourselves, but with others, rush in, and vapidity vanishes at once. Life, if it were to flow on for ever and *thus*, would stagnate and rot. The hopes, and fears, and regrets, which move and trouble it, keep it fresh and healthy, as the sea is kept alive by the trouble of its tides. In a tolerably comfortable world, where death is not, it is difficult to see from what quarter these healthful fears, regrets, and hopes could come. As it is, there are agitations and sufferings in our lots enough; but we must remember that it is on account of these sufferings and agitations that we become creatures breathing thoughtful breath. As has already been said, death takes away the commonplace of life. And positively, when one looks on the thousand and one poor, foolish, ignoble faces of this world, and listens to the chatter as poor and foolish as the faces, one, in order to have any proper respect for them, is forced to remember that solemnity of death, which is silently waiting. The foolishest person will look grand enough one day. The features are poor now, but the hottest tears and the most passionate embraces will not seem out of place *then*. If you wish to make a man look noble, your best course is to kill him. What superiority he may have inherited from his race, what superiority nature may have personally gifted him with, comes out in death. The passions which agitate, distort, and change, are gone away for ever, and the features settle back into a marble calm, which is the man's truest image. Then the most affected look sincere, the most volatile serious—all noble, more or less. And nature will not be surprised into disclosures. The man stretched out there may have been voluble as a swallow, but now—when he could speak to some purpose—neither pyramid nor sphinx holds a secret more tenaciously.

Consider, then, how the sense of impermanence brightens beauty and elevates happiness. Melancholy is always attendant on beauty, and that melancholy brings out its keenness as the dark-green corrugated leaf brings out the wan loveliness of the primrose. The spectator enjoys the beauty, but his knowledge that *it* is fleeting, and that *he* is fleeting, adds a pathetic something to it; and by that something the beautiful object and the gazer are alike raised.

Everything is sweetened by risk. The pleasant emotion is mixed and deepened by a sense of mortality. Those lovers who have never encountered the possibility of last embraces and farewells are novices in the passion. Sunset affects us more powerfully than sunrise, simply because it *is* a setting sun, and suggests a thousand analogies. A mother is never happier than when her eyes fill over her sleeping child, never does she kiss it more fondly, never does she pray for it more fervently; and yet there is more in her heart than visible red cheek and yellow curl; possession and bereavement are strangely mingled in the exquisite maternal mood, the one heightening the other. All great joys are serious; and emotion must be measured by its complexity and the deepness of its reach. A musician may draw pretty notes enough from a single key, but the richest music is that in which the whole force of the instrument is employed, in the production of which every key is vibrating; and, although full of solemn touches and majestic tones, the final effect may be exuberant and gay. Pleasures which rise beyond the mere gratification of the senses are dependent for their exquisiteness on the number and variety of the thoughts which they evoke. And that joy is the greatest which, while felt to be joy, can include the thought of death and clothe itself with that crowning pathos. And in the minds of thoughtful persons every joy does, more or less, with that crowning pathos clothe itself.

In life there is nothing more unexpected and

surprising than the arrivals and departures of pleasure. If we find it in one place to-day, it is vain to seek it there to-morrow. You cannot lay a trap for it. It will fall into no ambuscade, concert it ever so cunningly. Pleasure has no logic; it never treads in its own footsteps. Into our commonplace existence it comes with a surprise, like a pure white swan from the airy void into the ordinary village lake; and just as the swan, for no reason that can be discovered, lifts itself on its wings and betakes itself to the void again, *it* leaves us, and our sole possession is its memory. And it is characteristic of pleasure that we can never recognise it to be pleasure till after it is gone. Happiness never lays its finger on its pulse. If we attempt to steal a glimpse of its features it disappears. It is a gleam of unreckoned gold. From the nature of the case, our happiness, such as in its degree it has been, lives in memory. We have not the voice itself; we have only its echo. We are never happy; we can only remember that we were so once. And while in the very heart and structure of the happy moment there lurked an obscure consciousness of death, the memory in which past happiness dwells is always a regretful memory. This is why the tritest utterance about the past, youth, early love, and the like, has always about it an indefinable flavour of poetry, which pleases and affects. In the wake of a ship there is always a melancholy splendour. The finest set of verses of our modern time describes how the poet gazed on the "happy autumn fields," and remembered the "days that were no more." After all, a man's real possession is his memory. In nothing else is he rich, in nothing else is he poor.

In our warm imaginative youth, death is far removed from us, and attains thereby a certain picturesqueness. The grim thought stands in the ideal world as a ruin stands in a blooming landscape. The thought of death sheds a pathetic charm over everything then. The young man cools himself with a thought of the winding-sheet and the charnel, as the heated dancer cools himself on the balcony with the night-air. The young imagination plays with the idea of death, makes a toy of it, just as a child plays with edge-tools till once it cuts its fingers. The most lugubrious poetry is written by very young and tolerably comfortable persons. When a man's mood becomes really serious he has little taste for such foolery. The man who has a grave or two in his heart, does not need to haunt churchyards. The young poet uses death as an antithesis; and when he shocks his reader by some flippant use of it in that way, he considers he has written something mightily fine. In his gloomiest mood he is most insincere, most egotistical, most pretentious. The older and wiser poet avoids the subject as he does the memory of pain; or when he does refer to it, he does so in a reverential manner, and with some sense of its solemnity and of the magnitude of its issues. It was in that year of revelry, 1814, and while undressing from balls, that Lord Byron wrote his "Lara," as he informs us. Disrobing, and haunted, in all probability, by eyes in whose light he was happy enough, the spoiled young man, who then affected death-pallors, and wished the world to believe that he felt his richest wines powdered with the dust of graves—of which wine, notwithstanding, he frequently took more than was good for him—wrote,

That sleep the loveliest, since it dreams the least.

The sleep referred to being death. This was meant to take away the reader's breath; and after performing the feat, Byron betook himself to his pillow with a sense of supreme cleverness. Contrast with this Shakspeare's far out-looking and thought-heavy lines—lines which, under the same image, represent death—

To die—to sleep;—
To sleep! perchance to dream;—ay, there's the rub;
For in that sleep of death what dreams may come!

And you see at once how a man's notions of death and dying are deepened by a wider experience. Middle age may fear death quite as little as youth fears it; but it has learned seriousness, and it has no heart to poke fun at the lean ribs, or to call it fond names like a lover, or to stick a primrose in its grinning chaps, and draw a strange pleasure from the irrelevancy.

[62]

ON DEATH AND THE FEAR OF DYING

The man who has reached thirty, feels at times as if he had come out of a great battle. Comrade after comrade has fallen; his own life seems to have been charmed. And knowing how it fared with his friends—perfect health one day, a catarrh the next, blinds drawn down, silence in the house, blubbered faces of widow and orphans, intimation of the event in the newspapers, with a request that friends will accept of it, the day after—a man, as he draws near middle age, begins to suspect every transient indisposition; to be careful of being caught in a shower, to shudder at sitting in wet shoes; he feels his pulse, he anxiously peruses his face in a mirror, he becomes critical as to the colour of his tongue. In early life illness is a luxury, and draws out toward the sufferer curious and delicious tendernesses, which are felt to be a full over-payment of pain and weakness; then there is the pleasant period of convalescence, when one tastes a core and marrow of delight in meats, drinks, sleep, silence; the bunch of newly-plucked flowers on the table, the sedulous attentions and patient forbearance of nurses and friends. Later in life, when one occupies a post, and is in discharge of duties which are accumulating against recovery, illness and convalescence cease to be luxuries. Illness is felt to be a cruel interruption of the ordinary course of things, and the sick person is harassed by a sense of the loss of time and the loss of strength. He is placed *hors de combat*; all the while he is conscious that the battle is going on around him, and he feels his temporary withdrawal a misfortune. Of course, unless a man is very unhappily circumstanced, he has in his later illnesses all the love, patience, and attention which sweetened his earlier ones; but then he cannot rest in them, and accept them as before as compensation in full. The world is ever with him; through his interests and his affections he has meshed himself in an intricate net-work of relationships and other dependences, and a fatal issue—which in such cases is ever on the cards— would destroy all these, and bring about more serious matters than the shedding of tears. In a man's earlier illnesses, too, he had not only no such definite future to work out, he had a stronger spring of life and hope; he was rich in time, and could wait; and lying in his chamber now, he cannot help remembering that, as Mr. Thackeray expresses it, there comes at last an illness to which there may be no convalescence. What if that illness be already come? And so there is nothing left for him, but to bear the rod with patience, and to exercise a humble faith in the Ruler of all. If he recovers, some half-dozen people will be made happy; if he does not recover, the same number of people will be made miserable for a little while, and, during the next two or three days, acquaintances will meet in the street—"You've heard of poor So-and-so? Very sudden! Who would have thought it? Expect to meet you at ——'s on Thursday. Good-bye." And so the end.

ON DEATH AND THE FEAR OF DYING

Your death and my death are mainly of importance to ourselves. The black plumes will be stripped off our hearses within the hour; tears will dry, hurt hearts close again, our graves grow level with the churchyard, and although we are away, the world wags on. It does not miss us; and those who are near us, when the first strangeness of vacancy wears off, will not miss us much either.

We are curious as to death-beds and death-bed sayings; we wish to know how the matter stands; how the whole thing looks to the dying. Unhappily—perhaps, on the whole, happily—we can gather no information from these. The dying are nearly as reticent as the dead. The inferences we draw from the circumstances of death, the pallor, the sob, the glazing eye, are just as likely to mislead us as not. Manfred exclaims, "Old man, 'tis not so difficult to die!" Sterling wrote Carlyle "that it was all very strange, yet not so strange as it seemed to the lookers on." And so, perhaps, on the whole it is. The world has lasted six thousand years now, and, with the exception of those at present alive, the millions who have breathed upon it—splendid emperors, horny-fisted clowns, little children in whom thought has never stirred —*have* died, and what they have done, we also shall be able to do. It may not be so difficult, may not be so terrible, as our fears whisper. The dead keep their secrets, and in a little while we shall be as wise as they—and as taciturn.

WILLIAM DUNBAR

IF IT be assumed that the North Briton is, to an appreciable extent, a different creature from the Englishman, the assumption is not likely to provoke dispute. No one will deny us the prominence of our cheek-bones, and our pride in the same. How far the difference extends, whether it involves merit or demerit, are questions not now sought to be settled. Nor is it important to discover how the difference arose; how far chiller climate and sourer soil, centuries of unequal yet not inglorious conflict, a separate race of kings, a body of separate traditions, and a peculiar crisis of reformation issuing in peculiar forms of religious worship, confirmed and strengthened the national idiosyncrasy. If a difference between the races be allowed, it is sufficient for the present purpose. *That* allowed, and Scot and Southern being fecund in literary genius, it becomes an interesting inquiry to what extent the great literary men of the one race have influenced the great literary men of the other. On the whole, perhaps, the two races may fairly cry quits. Not unfrequently, indeed, have literary influences arisen in the north and travelled southwards. There were the Scottish ballads, for instance, there was Burns, there was Sir Walter Scott, there is Mr. Carlyle. The literary influence represented by each of these arose in Scotland, and has either passed or is passing "in music out of sight" in England. The energy of the northern wave has rolled into the southern waters. On the other hand, we can mark the literary influences travelling from the south northward. The English Chaucer rises, and the current of his influence is long afterwards visible in the Scottish King James, and the Scottish poet Dunbar. That which was Prior and Gay in London, became Allan Ramsay when it reached Edinburgh. Inspiration, not unfrequently, has travelled, like summer, from the south northwards; just as, when the day is over, and the lamps are lighted in London, the radiance of the setting sun is lingering on the splintered peaks and rosy friths of the Hebrides. All this, however, is a matter of the past; literary influence can no longer be expected to travel leisurely from south to north, or from north to south. In times of literary activity, as at the beginning of the present century, the atmosphere of passion or speculation envelops the entire island, and Scottish and English writers simultaneously draw from it what their peculiar natures prompt—just as in the same garden the rose drinks crimson and the convolvulus azure from the superincumbent air.

Chaucer must always remain a name in British literary history. He appeared at a time when the Saxon and Norman races had become fused, and when ancient bitternesses were lost in the proud title of Englishman. He was the first great poet the island produced; and he wrote for the most part in the language of the people, with just the slightest infusion of the courtlier Norman element, which gives to his writings something of the high-bred air that the short upper-lip gives to the human countenance. In his earlier poems he was under the influence of the Provençal Troubadours, and in his "Flower and the Leaf," and other works of a similar class, he riots in allegory; he represents the cardinal virtues walking about in human shape; his forests are full of beautiful ladies with coronals on their heads; courts of love are held beneath the spreading elm, and meta-physical goldfinches and nightingales, perched among the branches green, wrangle melodiously about the tender passion. In these poems he is fresh, charming, fanciful as the spring-time itself: ever picturesque, ever musical, and with a homely touch and stroke of irony here and there, suggesting a depth of serious matter in him which it needed years only to develop. He lived in a brilliant and stirring time; he was connected with the court; he served in armies; he visited the Continent; and, although a silent man, he carried with him, wherever he went, and into whatever company he was thrown, the most observant eyes perhaps that ever looked curiously out upon the world. There was nothing too mean or too trivial for his regard. After parting with a man, one fancies that he knew every line and wrinkle of his face, had marked the travel-stains on his boots, and had counted the slashes on his doublet. And so it was that, after mixing in kings' courts, and sitting with friars in taverns, and talking with people on country roads, and travelling in France and Italy, and making himself master of the literature, science, and theology of his time, and when perhaps touched with misfortune and sorrow, he came to see the depth of interest that resides in actual life—that the rudest clown even, with his sordid humours and coarse speech, is intrinsically more valuable than a whole forest full of goddesses, or innumerable processions of cardinal virtues, however well mounted and splendidly attired. It was in some such mood of mind that Chaucer penned those unparalleled pictures of contemporary life that delight yet, after five centuries have come and gone. It is difficult to define Chaucer's charm. He does not indulge in fine sentiment; he has no bravura passages; he is ever master of himself and of his subject. The light upon his page is the light of common day. Although powerful delineations of passion may be found in his "tales," and wonderful descriptions of nature, and although certain of the passages relating to Constance and Griselda in their deep distresses are unrivalled in tender-

ness, neither passion, nor natural description, nor
pathos, are his striking characteristics. It is his
shrewdness, his conciseness, his ever-present humour, his frequent irony, and his short, homely
line—effective as the play of the short Roman
sword—which strikes the reader most. In the
"Prologue to the Canterbury Tales"—by far the
ripest thing he has done—he seems to be writing
the easiest, most idiomatic prose, but it is poetry
all the while. He is a poet of natural manner,
dealing with outdoor life. Perhaps, on the whole,
the writer who most resembles him—superficial
differences apart—is Fielding. In both there is
constant shrewdness and common sense, a constant feeling of the comic side of things, a moral
instinct which escapes in irony, never in denunci-
ation or fanaticism; no remarkable spirituality of
feeling, an acceptance of the world as a pleasant
enough place, provided good dinners and a suf-
ficiency of cash are to be had, and that healthy
relish for fact and reality, and scorn of humbug
of all kinds, especially of that particular phase of
it which makes one appear better than one is,
which—for want of a better term—we are accustomed to call *English*. Chaucer was a Conserva-
tive in all his feelings; he liked to poke his fun at
the clergy, but he was not of the stuff of which
martyrs are made. He loved good eating and
drinking, and studious leisure and peace; and
although in his ordinary moods shrewd, and observant, and satirical, his higher genius would

now and then splendidly assert itself—and behold the tournament at Athens, where kings are combatants and Emily the prize; or the little boat, containing the brain-bewildered Constance and her child, wandering hither and thither on the friendly sea.

Chaucer was born about 1328, and died about 1380; and although he had, both in Scotland and England, contemporaries and immediate successors, no one of them can be compared with him for a moment. The "Moral Gower" was his friend, and inherited his tediousness and pedantry without a sparkle of his fancy, passion, humour, wisdom, and good spirits. Occleve and Lydgate followed in the next generation; and although their names are retained in literary histories, no line or sentence of theirs has found a place in human memory. The Scottish contemporary of Chaucer was Barbour, who, although deficient in tenderness and imagination, deserves praise for his sinewy and occasionally picturesque verse. "The Bruce" is really a fine poem. The hero is noble, resolute, and wise. Sir James Douglas is a very perfect, gentle knight. The old Churchman had the true poetic fire in him. He rises into eloquence in an apostrophe to Freedom, and he fights the battle of Bannockburn over again with great valour, shouting, and flapping of standards. In England, nature seemed to have exhausted herself in Chaucer, and she lay quiescent till Lord Surrey and Sir Thomas Wyatt came, the immediate precursors of Spenser, Shakspeare, and their companions.

While in England the note of the nightingale suddenly ceased, to be succeeded by the mere chirping of barn-door sparrows, the divine and melancholy voice began to be heard further north. It was during that most barren period of English poetry—extending from Chaucer's death till the beginning of Elizabeth's reign—that Scottish poetry arose, suddenly, splendidly—to be matched only by that other uprising nearer our own time, equally unexpected and splendid, of Burns and Scott. And it is curious to notice in this brilliant outburst of northern genius how much is owing to Chaucer; the cast of language is identical, the literary form is the same, there is the same way of looking at nature, the same allegorical forests, the troops of ladies, the same processions of cardinal virtues. James I, whose long captivity in England made him acquainted with Chaucer's works, was the leader of the poetic movement which culminated in Dunbar, and died away in Sir David Lindsay just before the noise and turmoil of the Reformation set in. In the concluding stanza of the "Quair," James records his obligation to those—

> *Masters dear,*
> *Gower and Chaucer, that on the steppes sate*
> *Of retorick, while they were livand here,*
> *Superlative as poets laureate*
> *Of morality and eloquence ornate.*

But while, during the reigns of the Jameses, Scottish genius was being acted upon by the broader and deeper genius of England, Scotland, quite unconsciously to herself, was preparing a liquidation in full of all spiritual obligations. For even then, in obscure nooks and corners, the Scottish ballads were growing up, quite uncontrolled by critical rules, rude in structure and expression, yet, at the same time, full of vitality, retaining in all their keenness the mirth of rustic festivals, and the piteousness of domestic tragedies. The stormy feudal time out of which they arose crumbled by process of gradual decay, but they remained, made brighter by each succeeding summer, like the wild-flowers that blow in the chinks of ruins. And when English poetry had become artificial and cold, the lucubrations of forgotten Scottish minstrels, full of the touches that make the whole world kin, brought new life with them. Scotland had invaded England more than once, but the blue bonnets never went over the border so triumphantly as when they did so in the shape of songs and ballads.

James IV, if not the wisest, was certainly the most brilliant monarch of his name; and he was fortunate beyond the later Stuarts in this, that during his lifetime no new popular tide had set in which it behoved him to oppose or to float upon. For him in all its essentials to-day had flowed quietly out of yesterday, and he lived unperplexed by fear of change. With something of a Southern gaiety of spirit, he was a merrier monarch than his dark-featured and saturnine descendant who bore the appellation. He was fond of martial sports, he loved to glitter at tournaments, his court was crowded with singing men and singing women. Yet he had his gloomy moods and superstitious despondencies. He could not forget that he had appeared in arms against his father; even while he whispered in the ear of beauty the iron belt of penance was fretting his side, and he alternated the splendid revel with the cell of the monk. In these days, and for long after, the Borders were disturbed, and the Highland clans, setting authority at defiance, were throttling each other in their mists. The Catholic religion was yet unsapped, and the wealth of the country resided in the hands of the nobles and the churchmen. Edinburgh towered high on the ridge between Holyrood and the Castle, its streets reddened with feud at intervals, and its merchants clustering round the Cathedral of St. Giles like bees in a honeycomb; and the king, when he looked across the faint azure of the Forth, beheld the long coast of Fife dotted with little towns, where ships were moored that traded with France and Holland, and brought with them cargoes of silks and wines. James was a popular monarch; he was beloved by the nobles and by the people. He loved justice, he cultivated his marine, and he built the *Great Michael*—the *Great Eastern* of that day. He had valiant seamen, and more than once Barton sailed into Leith with a string of English prizes. When he fell with all his nobility at Flodden, there came upon Scotland the woe with which she was so familiar—

Woe to that realme that haith an ower young king.

A long regency followed; disturbing elements of religion entered into the life of the nation, and the historical stream which had flowed smoothly for a series of years became all at once convulsed and turbulent, as if it had entered upon a gorge of rapids. It was in this pleasant interregnum of the reign of the fourth James, when ancient disorders had to a certain extent been repressed, and when religious difficulties ahead were yet undreamed of, that the poet Dunbar flourished— a nightingale singing in a sunny lull of the Scottish historical storm.

Modern readers are acquainted with Dunbar chiefly through the medium of Mr. David Laing's beautiful edition of his works published in 1834, and by good Dr. Irving's intelligent and admirably compacted "History of Scottish Poetry," published the other day. Irving's work, if deficient somewhat in fluency and grace of style, is characterised by conscientiousness of statement and by the ripest knowledge. Yet, despite the researches of these competent writers, of the events of the poet's life not much is known. He was born about

1460, and from an unquotable allusion in one of his poems, he is supposed to have been a native of the Lothians. His name occurs in the register of the University of St. Andrews as a Bachelor of Arts. With the exception of these entries in the college register, there is nothing authentically known of his early life. We have no portrait of him, and cannot by that means decipher him. We do not know with certainty from what family he sprang. Beyond what light his poems may throw on them, we have no knowledge of his habits and personal tastes. He exists for the most part in rumour, and the vague shadows of things. It appears that in early life he became a friar of the order of St. Francis; and in the capacity of a travelling priest he tells us that "he preached in Derntown kirk and in Canterbury"; that he "passed at Dover across the Channel, and went through Picardy teaching the people." He does not seem to have taken kindly to his profession. His works are full of sarcastic allusions to the clergy, and in no measured terms he denounces their luxury, their worldly-mindedness, and their desire for high place and fat livings. Yet these denunciations have no very spiritual origin. His rage is the rage of a disappointed candidate, rather than of a prophet; and, to the last, he seems to have expected preferment in the Church. Not without a certain pathos he writes, when he had become familiar with disappointment, and the sickness of hope deferred—

WILLIAM DUNBAR

I wes in youth an nureiss knee,
Dandely! bischop, dandely!
And quhen that age now dois me greif,
Ane sempill vicar I can nocht be.

It is not known when he entered the service of
King James. From his poems it appears that he
was employed as a clerk or secretary in several
of the missions despatched to foreign courts. It
is difficult to guess in what capacity Dunbar
served at Holyrood. He was all his life a priest,
and expected preferment from his royal patron.
We know that he performed mass in the presence.
Yet when the king in one of his dark moods had
withdrawn from the gaieties of the capital to the
religious gloom of the convent of Franciscans at
Stirling, we find the poet inditing a parody on the
machinery of the Church, calling on Father, Son,
and Holy Spirit, and on all the saints of the
calendar, to transport the princely penitent from
Stirling, "where ale is thin and small," to Edinburgh, where there is abundance of swans, cranes,
and plovers, and the fragrant clarets of France.
And in another of his poems, he describes himself
as dancing in the Queen's chamber so zealously
that he lost one of his slippers, a mishap which
provoked her Majesty to great mirth. Probably,
as the king was possessed of considerable literary
taste, and could appreciate Dunbar's fancy and
satire, he kept him attached to his person, with
the intention of conferring a benefice on him when

one fell vacant; and when a benefice *did* fall vacant,
felt compelled to bestow it on the cadet of some
powerful family in the state—for it was always the
policy of James to stand well with his nobles. He
remembered too well the deaths of his father and
great-grandfather to give unnecessary offence to
his great barons. From his connexion with the
court, the poet's life may be briefly epitomised.
In August 1500, his royal master granted Dunbar
an annual pension of £10 for life, or till such time
as he should be promoted to a benefice of the annual value of £40. In 1501, he visited England in
the train of the ambassadors sent thither to
negotiate the king's marriage. The marriage took
place in May 1503, on which occasion the high-
piled capital wore holiday attire, balconies blazed
with scarlet cloth, and the loyal multitude shouted
as bride and bridegroom rode past, with the
chivalry of two kingdoms in their train. Early
in May, Dunbar composed his most celebrated
poem in honour of the event. Next year he said
mass in the king's presence for the first time, and
received a liberal reward. In 1505, he received a
sum in addition to his stated pension, and two
years thereafter his pension was doubled. In August 1510, his pension was increased to £80 per
annum, until he became possessed of a benefice
of the annual value of £100 or upwards. In 1513,
Flodden was fought, and in the confusion conse-
quent on the king's death, Dunbar and his slowly-
increasing pensions disappear from the records of

things. We do not know whether he received his benefice; we do not know the date of his death, and to this day his grave is secret as the grave of Moses.

Knowing but little of Dunbar's life, our interest is naturally concentrated on what of his writings remain to us. And to modern eyes the old poet is a singular spectacle. His language is different from ours; his mental structure and modes of thought are unfamiliar; in his intellectual world, as we map it out to ourselves, it is difficult to conceive how a comfortable existence could be attained. Times, manners, and ideas have changed, and we look upon Dunbar with a certain reverential wonder and curiosity as we look upon Tantallon, standing up, grim and gray, in the midst of the modern landscape. The grand old fortress is a remnant of a state of things which have utterly passed away. Curiously, as we walk beside it, we think of the actual human life its walls contained. In those great fire-places logs actually burned once, and in winter nights men-at-arms spread out big palms against the grateful heat. In those empty apartments was laughter, and feasting, and serious talk enough in troublous times, and births, and deaths, and the bringing home of brides in their blushes. This empty moat was filled with water, to keep at bay long-forgotten enemies, and yonder loop-hole was made narrow, as a protection from long-mouldered arrows. In Tantallon we know the Douglasses lived in state, and bearded kings, and hung out banners to the breeze; but a sense of wonder is mingled with our knowledge, for the bothy of the Lothian farmer is even more in accordance with our methods of conducting life. Dunbar affects us similarly. We know that he possessed a keen intellect, a blossoming fancy, a satiric touch that blistered, a melody that enchanted Northern ears; but then we have lost the story of his life, and from his poems, with their wonderful contrasts, the delicacy and spring-like flush of feeling, the piety, the freedom of speech, the irreverent use of the sacredest names, the "Flyting" and the "Lament for the Makars," there is difficulty in making one's ideas of him cohere. He is present to the imagination, and yet remote. Like Tantallon, he is a portion of the past. We are separated from him by centuries, and that chasm we are unable to bridge properly.

The first thing that strikes the reader of these poems is their variety and intellectual range. It may be said that—partly from constitutional turn of thought, partly from the turbulent and chaotic time in which he lived, when families rose to splendour and as suddenly collapsed, when the steed that bore his rider at morning to the hunting-field returned at evening masterless to the castle-gate—Dunbar's prevailing mood of mind is melancholy; that he, with a certain fondness for the subject, as if it gave him actual relief, moralised over the sandy foundations of mortal prosperity, the advance of age putting out the lights of youth, and cancelling the rapture of the lover, and the certainty of death. This is a favourite path of contemplation with him, and he pursues it with a gloomy sedateness of acquiescence, which is more affecting than if he raved and foamed against the inevitable. But he has the mobility of the poetic nature, and the sad ground-tone is often drowned in the ecstasy of lighter notes. All at once the "bare ruined choirs" are covered with the glad light-green of spring. His genius combined the excellencies of many masters. His "Golden Targe" and the "Thistle and the Rose" are allegorical poems, full of colour, fancy, and music. His "Two Married Women and the Widow" has a good deal of Chaucer's slyness and humour. "The Dance of the Deadly Sins," with its fiery bursts of imaginative energy, its pictures finished at a stroke, is a prophecy of Spenser and Collins, and as fine as anything they have accomplished; while his "Flytings" are torrents of the coarsest vituperation. And there are whole flights of occasional poems, many of them sombre-coloured enough, with an ever-recurring mournful refrain, others satirical, but all flung off, one can see, at a sitting; in the few verses the mood is exhausted, and while the result remains, the cause is forgotten even by himself. Several of these short poems are almost perfect in feeling and execution. The melancholy ones are full of a serious grace, while in the satirical a laughing devil of glee and malice sparkles in every line. Some of these latter are dangerous to touch as a thistle—all bristling and angry with the spikes of satiric scorn.

In his allegorical poems—"The Golden Targe," "The Merle and the Nightingale," "The Thistle and the Rose,"—Dunbar's fancy has full scope. As allegories, they are, perhaps, not worth much; at all events, modern readers do not care for the adventures of "Quaking Dread and Humble Obedience"; nor are they affected by descriptions of Beauty, attended by her damsels, Fair Having, Fine Portraiture, Pleasance, and Lusty Cheer. The whole conduct and machinery of such things are too artificial and stilted for modern tastes. Stately masques are no longer performed in earls' mansions; and when a sovereign enters a city, a fair lady, with wings, representing Loyalty, does not burst out of a pasteboard cloud and recite a poetical address to Majesty. In our theatres the pantomime, which was originally an adumbration of human life, has become degraded. Symbolism has departed from the boards, and burlesque reigns in its stead. The Lord Mayor's Show, the last remnant of the antique spectacular taste, does not move us now; it is held a public nuisance; it provokes the rude "chaff" of the streets. Our very mobs have become critical. Gog and Magog are dethroned. The knight feels the satiric comments through his armour. The very steeds are uneasy, as if ashamed. But in Dunbar the allegorical machinery is saved from contempt by colour, poetry, and music. Quick surprises of beauty, and a rapid succession of pictures, keep the attention awake. Now it is—

> May, of mirthful monethis queen,
> Betwixt April and June, her sisters sheen,
> Within the garden walking up and down.

Now—

> The god of windis, Eolus,
> With variand look, richt like a lord unstable.

Now the nightingale—

> Never sweeter noise was heard with livand man,
> Nor made this merry, gentle nightingale;
> Her sound went with the river as it ran
> Out throw the fresh and flourished lusty vale.

And now a spring morning—

> Ere Phoebus was in purple cape revest,
> Up raise the lark, the heaven's minstrel fine
> In May, in till a morrow mirthfullest.

> Full angel-like thir birdis sang their hours
> Within their curtains green, in to their bours
> Apparelled white and red with bloomes sweet;
> Enamelled was the field with all colours,
> The pearly droppis shook in silver shours;
> While all in balm did branch and leavis fleet.
> To part fra Phoebus did Aurora greet,
> Her crystal tears I saw hing on the flours,
> Whilk he for love all drank up with his heat.

For mirth of May, with skippis and with hops,
The birdis sang upon the tender crops,
  With curious notes, as Venus' chapel clerks;
The roses young, new spreading of their knops,
Were powderit bricht with heavenly beriall drops,
  Through beames red, burning as ruby sparks;
  The skies rang for shouting of the larks,
The purple heaven oure scal't in silver slops,
  Ouregilt the trees, branches, leaves, and barks.

The finest of Dunbar's poems in this style is the
"Thistle and the Rose." It was written in celebration of the marriage of James with the Princess
Margaret of England, and the royal pair are happily represented as the national emblems. It, of
course, opens with a description of a spring morning. Dame Nature resolves that every bird, beast,
and flower should compeer before her highness; the
roe is commanded to summon the animals, the
restless swallow the birds, and the "conjured"
yarrow the herbs and flowers. In the twinkling
of an eye they stand before the queen. The lion
and the eagle are crowned, and are instructed to
be humble and just, and to exercise their powers
mercifully:—

Then callit she all flouris that grew in field,
  Discerning all their seasons and effeirs;
Upon the awful thistle she beheld
  And saw him keepit with a bush of spears:
  Consid'ring him so able for the weirs,

[84]

A radius crown of rubies she him gave,
And said, "In field, go forth and fend the lave."

The rose, also, is crowned, and the poet gives
utterance to the universal joy on occasion of the
marriage—type of peace between two kingdoms.
Listen to the rich music of according voices:—

Then all the birds sang with voice on hicht,
    Whose mirthful soun' was marvellous to hear;
The mavis sang, Hail Rose, most rich and richt,
    That does up flourish under Phoebus' sphere,
    Hail, plant of youth, hail Princess, dochter dear;
Hail blosom breaking out of the bluid royal,
Whose precious virtue is imperial.

The merle she sang, Hail, Rose of most delight,
    Hail, of all floris queen an' sovereign!
The lark she sang, Hail, Rose both red and white;
    Most pleasant flower, of michty colours twane:
    The nichtingale sang, Hail, Nature's suffragane,
In beauty, nurture, and every nobleness,
In rich array, renown, and gentleness.

The common voice up raise of birdes small,
    Upon this wise, Oh, blessit be the hour
That thou was chosen to be our principal!
    Welcome to be our Princess of honour,
    Our pearl, our pleasance, and our paramour,
Our peace, our play, our plain felicity;
Christ thee conserf from all adversity.

vision he heard Mahoun command that the
wretched who "had ne'er been shriven" should
dance before him. Immediately a hideous rout
present themselves; "holy harlots" appear in their
finery, and never a smile wrinkles the faces of the
onlookers; but when a string of "priests with their
shaven necks" come in, the arches of the unname-
able place shake with the laughter of all the fiends.
Then "The Seven Deadly Sins" began to leap at
once:—

> *And first of all the dance was Pride,*
> *With hair wyld back and bonnet on side.*

He, with all his train, came skipping through the
fire.

> *Then Ire came in with sturt and strife;*
> *His hand was aye upon his knife;*

and with him came armed boasters and braggarts,
smiting each other with swords, jagging each other
with knives. Then Envy, trembling with secret
hatred, accompanied by his court of flatterers,
backbiters, and calumniators, and all the human
serpentry that lurk in the palaces of kings. Then
came Covetousness, with his hoarders and misers,
and these the fiends gave to drink of newly-molten
gold.

Syne Swearness, at the second bidding,
Came like a sow out of a midding:

and with him danced a sleepy crew, and Belial lashed them with a bridle-rein, and the fiends gave them a turn in the fire to make them nimbler. Then came Lechery, led by Idleness, with a host of evil companions, "full strange of countenance, like torches burning bright." Then came Gluttony, so unwieldy that he could hardly move:—

Him followed mony foul drunkart
With can and callop, cup and quart,
In surfeit and excess.

"Drink, aye they cried," with their parched lips; and the fiends gave them hot lead to lap. Minstrels, it appears, are not to be found in that dismal place:—

Nae minstrels played to them but doubt,
For gleemen there were halden out
By day and eik by nicht:
Except a minstrel that slew a man,
So to his heritage he wan,
And entered by brieve of richt.

And to the music of the solitary poet in hell, the strange shapes pass. The conclusion of this singular poem is entirely farcical. The devil is resolved to make high holiday:—

Then cried Mahoun for a Hielan Padyane,
Syne ran a fiend to fetch Makfadyane,
* Far northwart in a neuck;*
Be he the coronach had done shout,
Ersche men so gatherit him about,
* In hell great room they took.*
Thae tarmigants, with tag and tatter,
Full loud in Ersche begoud to clatter,
* And roup like raven and rook.*
The Devil sae deaved was with their yell,
That in the deepest pot of hell
* He smorit them with smook.*

There is one other poem of Dunbar's which may be quoted as a contrast to what has been already given. It is remarkable as being the only one in which he assumes the character of a lover. The style of thought is quite modern; bereave it of its uncouth orthography, and it might have been written to-day. It is turned with much skill and grace. The constitutional melancholy of the man comes out in it; as, indeed, it always does when he finds a serious topic. It possesses more tenderness and sentiment than is his usual. It is the night-flower among his poems, breathing a mournful fragrance:—

Sweit rose of vertew and of gentilnes,
Delytsum lyllie of everie lustynes,
* Richest in bontie, and in beutie cleir,*
* And every vertew that to hevin is dear,*
Except onlie that ye ar mercyles,

Into your garthe this day I did persew:
Thair saw I flowris that fresche wer of hew,
Baith quhyte and reid most lustye wer to seyne,
And halsum herbis upone stalkis grene:
Yet leif nor flour fynd could I nane of rew.

I doute that March, with his cauld blastis keyne,
Hes slane this gentill herbe, that I of mene;
Quhois pitewous deithe dois to my hart sic pane,
That I wald mak to plant his rute agane,
So comfortand his levis unto me bene.

The extracts already given will enable the reader
to form some idea of the old poet's general power—
his music, his picturesque faculty, his colour, his
satire. Yet it is difficult from what he has left to
form any very definite image of the man. Although
his poems are for the most part occasional, founded
upon actual circumstances, or written to relieve
him from the over-pressure of angry or melancholy
moods, and although the writer is by no means
shy or indisposed to speak of himself, his personality is not made clear to us. There is a great gap
of time between him and the modern reader; and
the mixture of gold and clay in the products of his
genius, the discrepancy of elements, beauty, and
coarseness, Apollo's cheek, and the satyr's shaggy
limbs, are explainable partly from a want of harmony and completeness in himself, and partly from
the pressure of the half-barbaric time. His rudeness
offends, his narrowness astonishes. But then we

[91]

must remember that our advantages in these respects do not necessarily arise from our being of a purer and nobler essence. We have these things by inheritance; they have been transmitted to us along a line of ancestors. Five centuries share with us the merit of the result. Modern delicacy of taste and intellectual purity—although we hold them in possession, and may add to their sheen before we hand them on to our children—are no more to be placed to our personal credits than Dryden's satire, Pope's epigram, Marlborough's battles, Burke's speeches, and the victories of Trafalgar and Waterloo. Intellectual delicacy has grown like our political constitution. The English duke is not the creator of his own wealth, although in his keeping it makes the earth around him a garden, and the walls of his house bright with pictures. But our inability to conceive satisfactorily of Dunbar does not arise from this alone. We have his works, but then they are not supplemented by personal anecdote and letters, and the reminiscences of contemporaries. Burns, for instance, if limited to his works for our knowledge of him, would be a puzzling phenomenon. He was in his poems quite as outspoken as Dunbar, but then they describe so wide an area, they appear so contradictory, they seem often to lead in opposite directions. It is, to a large extent, through his letters that Burns is known; through his short, careless, pithy sayings, which imbedded themselves in the memories of his hearers; from the recollections of his contemporaries and their expressed judgments, and the multiform reverberations of fame lingering around such a man—these fill up interstices between works, bring apparent opposition into intimate relationship, and make wholeness out of confusion. Not on the stage alone, in the world also, a man's real character comes out best in his asides. With Dunbar there is nothing of this. He is a name, and little more. He exists in a region to which rumour and conjecture have never penetrated. He was long neglected by his countrymen, and was brought to light as if by accident. He is the Pompeii of British poetry. We have his works, but they are like the circumvallations of a Roman camp on the Scottish hillside. We see lines stretching hither and thither, but we cannot make out the plan, or divine what purposes were served. We only know that every crumbled rampart was once a defence; that every half-obliterated fosse once swarmed with men; that it was once a station and abiding-place of human life, although for centuries now remitted to silence and blank summer sunshine.

A LARK'S FLIGHT

RIGHTLY or wrongly, during the last twenty or thirty years a strong feeling has grown up in the public mind against the principle, and a still stronger feeling against the practice, of capital punishments. Many people who will admit that the execution of the murderer may be, abstractly considered, just enough, sincerely doubt whether such execution be expedient, and are in their own minds perfectly certain that it cannot fail to demoralise the spectators. In consequence of this, executions have become rare; and it is quite clear that many scoundrels, well worthy of the noose, contrive to escape it. When, on the occasion of a wretch being turned off, the spectators are few, it is remarked by the newspapers that the mob is beginning to lose its proverbial cruelty, and to be stirred by humane pulses; when they are numerous, and especially when girls and women form a majority, the circumstance is noticed and deplored. It is plain enough that, if the newspaper considered such an exhibition beneficial, it would not lament over a few thousand eager witnesses: if the sermon be edifying, you cannot have too large a congregation; if you teach a moral lesson in a grand, impressive way, it is difficult to see how you can have too many pupils. Of course, neither the justice nor the expediency of capital punishments falls to be discussed here. This, however, may be said, that the popular feeling against them may not be so admirable a proof of enlightenment as many believe. It is true that the spectacle is painful, horrible; but in pain and horror there is often hidden a certain salutariness, and the repulsion of which we are conscious is as likely to arise from debilitation of public nerve, as from a higher reach of public feeling. To my own thinking, it is out of this pain and hatefulness that an execution becomes invested with an ideal grandeur. It is sheer horror to all concerned—sheriffs, halbertmen, chaplain, spectators, Jack Ketch, and culprit; but out of all this, and towering behind the vulgar and hideous accessories of the scaffold, gleams the majesty of implacable law. When every other fine morning a dozen cut-purses were hanged at Tyburn, and when such sights did not run very strongly against the popular current, the spectacle *was* vulgar, and could be of use only to the possible cut-purses congregated around the foot of the scaffold. Now, when the law has become so far merciful; when the punishment of death is reserved for the murderer; when he can be condemned only on the clearest evidence; when, as the days draw slowly on to doom, the frightful

event impending over one stricken wretch throws
its shadow over the heart of every man, woman,
and child in the great city; and when the official
persons whose duty it is to see the letter of the law
carried out perform that duty at the expense of
personal pain, a public execution is not vulgar,
it becomes positively sublime. It is dreadful, of
course; but its dreadfulness melts into pure awful-
ness. The attention is taken off the criminal, and is
lost in a sense of the grandeur of justice; and the
spectator who beholds an execution, solely as it
appears to the eye, without recognition of the idea
which towers behind it, must be a very unspiritual
and unimaginative spectator indeed.

It is taken for granted that the spectators of
public executions—the artisans and country people
who take up their stations over-night as close to
the barriers as possible, and the wealthier classes
who occupy hired windows and employ opera-
glasses—are merely drawn together by a morbid
relish for horrible sights. He is a bold man who will
stand forward as the advocate of such persons—so
completely is the popular mind made up as to their
tastes and motives. It is not disputed that the
large body of the mob, and of the occupants of
windows, have been drawn together by an appetite
for excitement; but it is quite possible that many
come there from an impulse altogether different.
Just consider the nature of the expected sight—a
man in tolerable health probably, in possession of
all his faculties, perfectly able to realise his posi-

tion, conscious that for him this world and the next are so near that only a few seconds divide them—such a man stands in the seeing of several thousand eyes. He is so peculiarly circumstanced, so utterly lonely—hearing the tolling of his own death-bell, yet living, wearing the mourning clothes for his own funeral—that he holds the multitude together by a shuddering fascination. The sight is a peculiar one, you must admit, and every peculiarity has its attractions. Your volcano is more attractive than your ordinary mountain. Then consider the unappeasable curiosity as to death which haunts every human being, and how pathetic that curiosity is, in so far as it suggests our own ignorance and helplessness, and we see at once that people *may* flock to public executions for other purposes than the gratification of morbid tastes: that they would pluck if they could some little knowledge of what death is; that imaginatively they attempt to reach to it, to touch and handle it through an experience which is not their own. It is some obscure desire of this kind, a movement of curiosity not altogether ignoble, but in some degree pathetic; some rude attempt of the imagination to wrest from the death of the criminal information as to the great secret in which each is profoundly interested, which draws around the scaffold people from the country harvest-fields, and from the streets and alleys of the town. Nothing interests men so much as death. Age cannot wither it, nor custom stale it. "A greater crowd would come to see me hanged,"

Cromwell is reported to have said when the populace came forth on a public occasion. The Lord Protector was right in a sense of which, perhaps, at the moment he was not aware. Death is greater than official position. When a man has to die, he may safely dispense with stars and ribbands. He is invested with a greater dignity than is held in the gift of kings. A greater crowd *would* have gathered to see Cromwell hanged, but the compliment would have been paid to death rather than to Cromwell. Never were the motions of Charles I so scrutinised as when he stood for a few moments on the scaffold that winter morning at Whitehall. King Louis was no great orator usually, but when on the 2d January 1793, he attempted to speak a few words in the Place de la Revolution, it was found necessary to drown his voice in a harsh roll of soldiers' drums. Not without a meaning do people come forth to see men die. We stand in the valley, they on the hilltop, and on their faces strikes the light of the other world, and from some sign or signal of theirs we attempt to discover or extract a hint of what it is all like.

To be publicly put to death, for whatever reason, must ever be a serious matter. It is always bitter, but there are degrees in its bitterness. It is easy to die like Stephen with an opened heaven above you, crowded with angel faces. It is easy to die like Balmerino with a chivalrous sigh for the White Rose, and an audible "God bless King James." Such men die for a cause in which they glory, and are supported thereby; they are conducted to the portals of the next world by the angels, Faith, Pity, Admiration. But it is not easy to die in expiation of a crime like murder, which engirdles you with trembling and horror even in the loneliest places, which cuts you off from the sympathies of your kind, which reduces the universe to two elements— a sense of personal identity, and a memory of guilt. In so dying, there must be inconceivable bitterness; a man can have no other support than what strength he may pluck from despair, or from the iron with which nature may have originally braced heart and nerve. Yet, taken as a whole, criminals on the scaffold comport themselves creditably. They look Death in the face when he wears his cruellest aspect, and if they flinch somewhat, they can at least bear to look. I believe that, for the criminal, execution within the prison walls, with no witnesses save some half-dozen official persons, would be infinitely more terrible than execution in the presence of a curious, glaring mob. The daylight and the publicity are alien elements, which wean the man a little from himself. He steadies his dizzy brain on the crowd beneath and around him. He has his last part to play, and his manhood rallies to play it well. Nay, so subtly is vanity intertwined with our motives, the noblest and the most ignoble, that I can fancy a poor wretch with the noose dangling at his ear, and with barely five minutes to live, soothed somewhat with the idea that his firmness and composure will earn him the

approbation, perhaps the pity, of the spectators.
He would take with him, if he could, the good
opinion of his fellows. This composure of criminals
puzzles one. Have they looked at death so long
and closely, that familiarity has robbed it of
terror? Has life treated them so harshly, that they
are tolerably well pleased to be quit of it on any
terms? Or is the whole thing mere blind stupor
and delirium, in which thought is paralysed, and
the man an automaton? Speculation is useless.
The fact remains that criminals for the most part
die well and bravely. It is said that the champion-
ship of England was to be decided at some little
distance from London on the morning of the day
on which Thurtell was executed, and that, when
he came out on the scaffold, he inquired privily
of the executioner if the result had yet become
known. Jack Ketch was not aware, and Thurtell
expressed his regret that the ceremony in which
he was chief actor should take place so incon-
veniently early in the day. Think of a poor Thurtell forced to take his long journey an hour,
perhaps, before the arrival of intelligence so important!

More than twenty years ago I saw two men
executed, and the impression then made remains
fresh to this day. For this there were many reasons.
The deed for which the men suffered created an
immense sensation. They were hanged on the spot
where the murder was committed—on a rising
ground, some four miles north-east of the city;

and as an attempt of rescue was apprehended, there was a considerable display of military force on the occasion. And when, in the dead silence of thousands, the criminals stood beneath the halters, an incident occurred, quite natural and slight in itself, but when taken in connexion with the business then proceeding, so unutterably tragic, so overwhelming in its pathetic suggestion of contrast, that the feeling of it has never departed, and never will. At the time, too, I speak of, I was very young; the world was like a die newly cut, whose every impression is fresh and vivid.

While the railway which connects two northern capitals was being built, two brothers from Ireland, named Doolan, were engaged upon it in the capacity of navvies. For some fault or negligence, one of the brothers was dismissed by the overseer— a Mr. Green—of that particular portion of the line on which they were employed. The dismissed brother went off in search of work, and the brother who remained—Dennis was the Christian name of him—brooded over this supposed wrong, and in his dull, twilighted brain revolved projects of vengeance. He did not absolutely mean to take Green's life, but he meant to thrash him to within an inch of it. Dennis, anxious to thrash Green, but not quite seeing his way to it, opened his mind one afternoon, when work was over, to his friends— fellow-Irishmen and navvies—Messrs. Redding and Hickie. These took up Doolan's wrong as their own, and that evening, by the dull light of a bothy fire, they held a rude parliament, discussing ways and means of revenge. It was arranged that Green should be thrashed—the amount of thrashing left an open question, to be decided, unhappily, when the blood was up and the cinder of rage blown into a flame. Hickie's spirit was found not to be a mounting one, and it was arranged that the active partners in the game should be Doolan and Redding. Doolan, as the aggrieved party, was to strike the · first blow, and Redding, as the aggrieved party's particular friend, asked and obtained permission to strike the second. The main conspirators, with a fine regard for the feelings of the weaker Hickie, allowed him to provide the weapons of assault—so that by some slight filament of aid he might connect himself with the good cause. The unambitious Hickie at once applied himself to his duty. He went out, and in due time returned with two sufficient iron pokers. The weapons were examined, approved of, and carefully laid aside. Doolan, Redding, and Hickie ate their suppers, and retired to their several couches to sleep, peacefully enough no doubt. About the same time, too, Green, the English overseer, threw down his weary limbs, and entered on his last sleep—little dreaming what the morning had in store for him.

Uprose the sun, and uprose Doolan and Redding, and dressed, and thrust each his sufficient iron poker up the sleeve of his blouse, and went forth. They took up their station on a temporary wooden bridge which spanned the line, and waited there. Across the bridge, as was expected, did Green ultimately come. He gave them good morning; asked, "why they were loafing about?" received no very pertinent answer, perhaps did not care to receive one; whistled—the unsuspecting man!—thrust his hands into his breeches pockets, turned his back on them, and leaned over the railing of the bridge, inspecting the progress of the works beneath. The temptation was really too great. What could wild Irish flesh and blood do? In a moment out from the sleeve of Doolan's blouse came the hidden poker, and the first blow was struck, bringing Green to the ground. The friendly Redding, who had bargained for the second, and who, naturally enough, was in fear of being cut out altogether, jumped on the prostrate man, and fulfilled his share of the bargain with a will. It was Redding it was supposed who sped the unhappy Green. They overdid their work —like young authors—giving many more blows than were sufficient, and then fled. The works, of course, were that morning in consternation. Redding and Hickie were, if I remember rightly, apprehended in the course of the day. Doolan got off, leaving no trace of his whereabouts.

These particulars were all learned subsequently. The first intimation which we schoolboys received of anything unusual having occurred, was the sight of a detachment of soldiers with fixed bayonets, trousers rolled up over muddy boots, marching past the front of the Cathedral hurriedly home

to barracks. This was a circumstance somewhat
unusual. We had, of course, frequently seen a
couple of soldiers trudging along with sloped
muskets, and that cruel glitter of steel which no
one of us could look upon quite unmoved; but in
such cases, the deserter walking between them
in his shirt-sleeves, his pinioned hands covered
from public gaze by the loose folds of his greatcoat, explained everything. But from the hurried
march of these mud-splashed men nothing could
be gathered, and we were left to speculate upon
its meaning. Gradually, however, before the evening fell, the rumour of a murder having been committed spread through the city, and with that
I instinctively connected the apparition of the file
of muddy soldiers. Next day, murder was in every
mouth. My schoolfellows talked of it to the detriment of their lessons; it flavoured the tobacco of
the fustian artizan as he smoked to work after
breakfast; it walked on 'Change amongst the
merchants. It was known that two of the persons
implicated had been captured, but that the other,
and guiltiest, was still at large; and in a few days
out on every piece of boarding and blank wall came
the "Hue and cry"—describing Doolan like a
photograph, to the colour and cut of his whiskers,
and offering £100 as reward for his apprehension,
or for such information as would lead to his apprehension—like a silent, implacable bloodhound
following close on the track of the murderer. This
terrible broadsheet I read, was certain that *he*

had read it also, and fancy ran riot over the ghastly fact. For him no hope, no rest, no peace, no touch of hands gentler than the hangman's; all the world is after him like a roaring prairie of flame! I thought of Doolan, weary, foot-sore, heart-sore, entering some quiet village of an evening; and to quench his thirst, going up to the public well, around which the gossips are talking, and hearing that they were talking of *him;* and seeing from the well itself, IT glaring upon him, as if conscious of his presence, with a hundred eyes of vengeance. I thought of him asleep in out-houses, and starting up in wild dreams of the policeman's hand upon his shoulder fifty times ere morning. He had committed the crime of Cain, and the weird of Cain he had to endure. But yesterday innocent, how unimportant; to-day bloody-handed, the whole world is talking of him, and everything he touches, the very bed he sleeps on, steals from him his secret, and is eager to betray!

Doolan was finally captured in Liverpool, and in the Spring Assize the three men were brought to trial. The jury found them guilty, but recommended Hickie to mercy on account of some supposed weakness of mind on his part. Sentence was, of course, pronounced with the usual solemnities. They were set apart to die; and when snug abed o' nights—for imagination is most mightily moved by contrast—I crept into their desolate hearts, and tasted a misery which was not my own. As already said, Hickie was recommended to mercy, and the recommendation was ultimately in the proper quarter given effect to.

The evening before the execution has arrived, and the reader has now to imagine the early May sunset falling pleasantly on the outskirts of the city. The houses looking out upon an open square or space, have little plots of garden-ground in their fronts, in which mahogany-coloured wall-flowers and mealy auriculas are growing. The side of this square, along which the City Road stretches northward, is occupied by a blind asylum, a brick building, the bricks painted red and picked out with white, after the tidy English fashion, and a high white cemetery wall, over which peers the spire of the Gothic Cathedral; and beyond that, on the other side of the ravine, rising out of a populous city of the dead, a stone John Knox looks down on the Cathedral, a Bible clutched in his outstretched and menacing hand. On all this the May sunset is striking, dressing everything in its warm, pleasant pink, lingering in the tufts of foliage that nestle around the asylum, and dipping the building itself one half in light, one half in tender shade. This open space or square is an excellent place for the games of us boys, and "Prisoners' Base" is being carried out with as much earnestness as the business of life now by those of us who are left. The girls, too, have their games of a quiet kind, which we hold in huge scorn and contempt. In two files, linked arm-in-arm, they alternately dance towards each other and then retire, singing the while, in their clear, girlish treble, verses, the meaning and pertinence of which time has worn away—

The Campsie Duke's a-riding, a-riding, a-riding,

being the oft-recurring "owercome" or refrain. All this is going on in the pleasant sunset light, when by the apparition of certain waggons coming up from the city, piled high with blocks and beams, and guarded by a dozen dragoons, on whose brazen helmets the sunset danced, every game is dismembered, and we are in a moment a mere mixed mob of boys and girls, flocking around to stare and wonder. Just at this place something went wrong with one of the waggon wheels, and the procession came to a stop. A crowd collected, and we heard some of the grown-up people say that the scaffold was being carried out for the ceremony of to-morrow. Then, more intensely than ever, one realised the condition of the doomed men. *We* were at our happy games in the sunset, *they* were entering on their last night on earth. After hammering and delay the wheel was put to rights, the sunset died out, waggons and dragoons got into motion and disappeared; and all the night through, whether awake or asleep, I saw the torches burning, and heard the hammers clinking, and witnessed as clearly as if I had been an onlooker, the horrid structure rising, till it stood complete, with a huge cross-beam from which two empty halters hung, in the early morning light.

Next morning the whole city was in commotion. Whether the authorities were apprehensive that a rescue would be attempted, or were anxious merely to strike terror into the hundreds of wild Irishry engaged on the railway, I cannot say; in any case, there was a display of military force quite unusual. The carriage in which the criminals —Catholics both—and their attendant priests were seated, was guarded by soldiers with fixed bayonets; indeed, the whole regiment then lying in the city was massed in front and behind, with a cold, frightful glitter of steel. Besides the foot soldiers, there were dragoons, and two pieces of cannon; a whole little army, in fact. With a slenderer force battles have been won which have made a mark in history. What did the prisoners think of their strange importance, and of the tramp and hurly-burly all around? When the procession moved out of the city, it seemed to draw with it almost the entire population; and when once the country roads were reached, the crowd spread over the fields on either side, ruthlessly treading down the tender wheat braird. I got a glimpse of the doomed, blanched faces which had haunted me so long, at the turn of the road, where, for the first time, the black cross-beam with its empty halters first became visible to them. Both turned and regarded it with a long, steady look; that done, they again bent their heads attentively to the words of the clergyman. I suppose in that long, eager, fascinated gaze they practically *died*—that for them death had no additional bitterness. When the mound was reached on which the scaffold stood, there was immense confusion. Around it a wide space was kept clear by the military; the cannon were placed in position; out flashed the swords of the dragoons; beneath and around on every side was the crowd. Between two brass helmets I could see the scaffold clearly enough, and when in a little while the men, bareheaded and with their attendants, appeared upon it, the surging crowd became stiffened with fear and awe. And now it was that the incident so simple, so natural, so much in the ordinary course of things, and yet so frightful in its tragic suggestions, took place. Be it remembered that the season was early May, that the day was fine, that the wheat-fields were clothing themselves in the green of the young crop, and that around the scaffold, standing on a sunny mound, a wide space was kept clear. When the men appeared beneath the beam, each under his proper halter, there was a dead silence—every one was gazing too intently to whisper to his neighbour even. Just then, out of the grassy space at the foot of the scaffold, in the dead silence audible to all, a lark rose from the side of its nest, and went singing upward in its happy flight. O heaven! how did that song translate itself into dying ears? Did it bring in one wild burning moment father, and mother, and poor Irish cabin, and prayers said at bed-time, and the smell of turf fires, and innocent sweethearting, and rising and setting suns?

Did it—but the dragoon's horse has become restive, and his brass helmet bobs up and down and blots everything; and there is a sharp sound, and I feel the great crowd heave and swing, and hear it torn by a sharp shiver of pity, and the men whom I saw so near but a moment ago are at immeasurable distance, and have solved the great enigma—and the lark has not yet finished his flight: you can see and hear him yonder in the fringe of a white May cloud.

This ghastly lark's flight, when the circumstances are taken into consideration, is, I am inclined to think, more terrible than anything of the same kind which I have encountered in books. The artistic uses of contrast as background and accompaniment, are well known to nature and the poets. Joy is continually worked on sorrow, sorrow on joy; riot is framed in peace, peace in riot. Lear and the Fool always go together. Trafalgar is being fought while Napoleon is sitting on horseback watching the Austrian army laying down its arms at Ulm. In Hood's poem, it is when looking on the released schoolboys at their games that Eugene Aram remembers he is a murderer. And these two poor Irish labourers could not die without hearing a lark singing in their ears. It is Nature's fashion. She never quite goes along with us. She is sombre at weddings, sunny at funerals, and she frowns on ninety-nine out of a hundred pic-nics.

There is a stronger element of terror in this

incident of the lark than in any story of a similar kind I can remember.

A good story is told of an Irish gentleman—still known in London society—who inherited the family estates and the family banshee. The estates he lost—no uncommon circumstance in the history of Irish gentlemen,—but the banshee, who expected no favours, stuck to him in his adversity, and crossed the channel with him, making herself known only on occasions of death-beds and sharp family misfortunes. This gentleman had an ear, and, seated one night at the opera, the *keen*— heard once or twice before on memorable occasions —thrilled through the din of the orchestra and the passion of the singers. He hurried home of course, found his immediate family well, but on the morrow a telegram arrived with the announcement of a brother's death. Surely of all superstitions that is the most imposing which makes the other world interested in the events which befall our mortal lot. For the mere pomp and pride of it, your ghost is worth a dozen retainers, and it is entirely inexpensive. The peculiarity and supernatural worth of this story lies in the idea of the old wail piercing through the sweet entanglement of stringed instruments and extinguishing Grisi. Modern circumstances and luxury crack, as it were, and reveal for a moment misty and aboriginal time big with portent. There is a ridiculous Scotch story in which one gruesome touch lives. A clergyman's female servant was seated in the kitchen one

Saturday night reading the Scriptures, when she
was somewhat startled by hearing at the door the
tap and voice of her sweetheart. Not expecting
him, and the hour being somewhat late, she opened
it in astonishment, and was still more astonished
to hear him on entering abuse Scripture-reading.
He behaved altogether in an unprecedented manner, and in many ways terrified the poor girl.
Ultimately he knelt before her, and laid his head
on her lap. You can fancy her consternation when
glancing down she discovered that, *instead of hair,
the head was covered with the moss of the moorland.*
By a sacred name she adjured him to tell who he
was, and in a moment the figure was gone. It was
the Fiend, of course—diminished sadly since
Milton saw him bridge chaos—fallen from worlds
to kitchen-wenches. But just think how in the
story, in half-pity, in half-terror, the popular feeling of homelessness, of being outcast, of being
unsheltered as waste and desert places, has incar-
nated itself in that strange covering of the head. It
is a true supernatural touch. One other story I have
heard in the misty Hebrides: A Skye gentleman
was riding along an empty moorland road. All at
once, as if it had sprung from the ground, the
empty road was crowded by a funeral procession.
Instinctively he drew his horse to a side to let it
pass, which it did without sound of voice, without
tread of foot. Then he knew it was an apparition.
Staring on it, he knew every person who either bore
the corpse or who walked behind as mourners.

There were the neighbouring proprietors at whose houses he dined, there were the members of his own kirk-session, there were the men to whom he was wont to give good-morning when he met them on the road or at market. Unable to discover his own image in the throng, he was inwardly marvelling whose funeral it *could* be, when the troop of spectres vanished, and the road was empty as before. Then, remembering that the coffin had an invisible occupant, he cried out, "It is my funeral!" and, with all his strength taken out of him, rode home to die. All these stories have their own touches of terror; yet I am inclined to think that my lark rising from the scaffold foot, and singing to two such auditors, is more terrible than any one of them.

CHRISTMAS

OVER the dial-face of the year, on which the hours are months, the apex resting in sunshine, the base in withered leaves and snows, the finger of time does not travel with the same rapidity. Slowly it creeps up from snow to sunshine; when it has gained the summit it seems almost to rest for a little; rapidly it rushes down from sunshine to the snow. Judging from my own feelings, the distance from January to June is greater than from June to January—the period from Christmas to Midsummer seems longer than the period from Midsummer to Christmas. This feeling arises, I should fancy, from the preponderance of *light* on that half of the dial on which the finger seems to be travelling upwards, compared with the half on which it seems to be travelling downwards. This light to the eye, the mind translates into time. Summer days are long, often wearisomely so. The long-lighted days are bracketed together by a little bar of twilight, in which but a star or two find time to twinkle. Usually one has less occupation in summer than in winter, and the surplusage of summer light, a stage too large for the play, wearies, oppresses, sometimes appals. From the sense of time we can only shelter ourselves by occupation; and when occupation ceases while yet some three or four hours of light remain, the burden falls down, and is often greater than we can bear. Personally, I have a certain morbid fear of those endless summer twilights. A space of light stretching from half-past 2 A. M. to 11 P. M. affects me with a sense of infinity, of horrid sameness, just as the sea or the desert would do. I feel that for too long a period I am under the eye of a taskmaster. Twilight is always in itself, or at least in its suggestions, melancholy; and these midsummer twilights are so long, they pass through such series of lovely change, they are throughout so mournfully beautiful, that in the brain they beget strange thoughts, and in the heart strange feelings. We see too much of the sky, and the long, lovely, pathetic, lingering evening light, with its suggestions of eternity and death, which one cannot for the soul of one put into words, is somewhat too much for the comfort of a sensitive human mortal. The day dies, and makes no apology for being such an unconscionable time in dying; and all the while it colours our thoughts with its own solemnity. There is no relief from this kind of thing at midsummer. You cannot close your shutters and light your candles; that in the tone of mind which circumstances superinduce would be brutality. You cannot take Pickwick to the window and read it by the dying light; that is profanation. If you have a friend with you, you can't talk; the hour makes you silent. You are driven in on your self-consciousness. The long light wearies the eye, a sense of time disturbs and saddens the spirit; and that is the reason, I think, that one half of the year seems so much longer than the other half; that on the dial-plate whose hours are months, the restless finger *seems* to move more slowly when travelling upward from autumn leaves and snow to light, than when it is travelling downward from light to snow and withered leaves.

Of all the seasons of the year, I like winter best. That peculiar burden of time I have been speaking of, does not affect me now. The day is short, and I can fill it with work; when evening comes, I have my lighted room and my books. Should black care haunt me, I throw it off the scent in Spenser's forests, or seek refuge from it among Shakspeare's men and women, who are by far the best company I have met with, or am like to meet with, on earth. I am sitting at this present moment with my curtains drawn; the cheerful fire is winking at all the furniture in the room, and from every leg and arm the furniture is winking to the fire in return. I put off the outer world with my greatcoat and boots, and put on contentment and idleness with my slippers. On the hearth-rug, Pepper, coiled in a shaggy ball, is asleep in the ruddy light and heat. An imaginative sense of the cold outside increases my present comfort—just as one never hugs one's

own good luck so affectionately as when listening
to the relation of some horrible misfortune which
has overtaken others. Winter has fallen on Dreamthorp, and it looks as pretty when covered with
snow, as when covered with apple blossom. Outside, the ground is hard as iron; and over the low
dark hill, lo! the tender radiance that precedes the
moon. Every window in the little village has its
light, and to the traveller coming on, enveloped in
his breath, the whole place shines like a congregation of glow-worms. A pleasant enough sight to
him if his home be there! At this present season,
the canal is not such a pleasant promenade as it
was in summer. The barges come and go as usual,
but at this time I do not envy the bargemen quite
so much. The horse comes smoking along; the tar-
paulin which covers the merchandise is sprinkled
with hoar frost; and the helmsman, smoking his
short pipe for the mere heat of it, cowers over a few
red cinders contained in a framework of iron. The
labour of the poor fellows will soon be over for a
time; for if this frost continues, the canal will be
sheathed in a night, and next day stones will be
thrown upon it, and a daring urchin venturing
upon it will go souse head over heels, and run home
with his teeth in a chatter; and the day after, the
lake beneath the old castle will be sheeted, and the
next, the villagers will be sliding on its gleaming
face from ruddy dawn at nine to ruddy eve at
three; and hours later, skaters yet unsatisfied will
be moving ghost-like in the gloom—now one, now

another, shooting on sounding irons into a clear space of frosty light, chasing the moon, or the flying image of a star! Happy youths leaning against the frosty wind!

I am a Christian I hope, although far from a muscular one—consequently I cannot join the skaters on the lake. The floor of ice, with the people upon it, will be but a picture to me. And, in truth, it is in its pictorial aspect that I chiefly love the bleak season. As an artist, winter can match summer any day. The heavy, feathery flakes have been falling all the night through, we shall suppose, and when you get up in the morning the world is draped in white. What a sight it is! It is the world you knew, but yet a different one. The familiar look has gone, and another has taken its place; and a not unpleasant puzzlement arises in your mind, born of the patent and the remembered aspect. It reminds you of a friend who has been suddenly placed in new circumstances, in whom there is much that you recognise, and much that is entirely strange. How purely, divinely white when the last snowflake has just fallen! How exquisite and virginal the repose! It touches you like some perfection of music. And winter does not work only on a broad scale; he is careful in trifles. Pluck a single ivy leaf from the old wall, and see what a jeweller he is! How he has silvered over the dark-green reticulations with his frosts! The faggot which the Tramp gathers for his fire is thicklier incrusted with gems than ever was sceptre of the

Moguls. Go into the woods, and behold on the black boughs his glories of pearl and diamond— pendant splendours that, smitten by the noon-ray, melt into tears and fall but to congeal into splendours again. Nor does he work in black and white alone. He has on his palette more gorgeous colours than those in which swim the summer setting suns; and with these, about three o'clock, he begins to adorn his west, sticking his red hot ball of a sun in the very midst; and a couple of hours later, when the orb has fallen, and the flaming crimson has mellowed into liquid orange, you can see the black skeletons of trees scribbled upon the melancholy glory. Nor need I speak of the magnificence of a winter midnight, when space, sombre blue, crowded with star and planet, "burnished by the frost," is glittering like the harness of an archangel full panoplied against a battle day.

For years and years now I have watched the seasons come and go around Dreamthorp, and each in its turn interests me as if I saw it for the first time. But the other week it seems that I saw the grain ripen; then by day a motley crew of reapers were in the fields, and at night a big red moon looked down upon the stooks of oats and barley; then in mighty wains the plenteous harvest came swaying home, leaving a largess on the roads for every bird; then the round, yellow, comfortable-looking stacks stood around the farm-houses, hiding them to the chimneys; then the woods reddened, the beech hedges became russet,

and every puff of wind made rustle the withered
leaves; then the sunset came before the early dark,
and in the east lay banks of bleak pink vapour,
which are ever a prophecy of cold; then out of a
low dingy heaven came all day, thick and silent,
the whirling snow;—and so by exquisite succession of sight and sound have I been taken from
the top of the year to the bottom of it, from midsummer, with its unreaped harvests, to the night
on which I am sitting here—Christmas 1862.

Sitting here, I incontinently find myself holding
a levee of departed Christmas nights. Silently, and
without special call, into my study of imagination
come these apparitions, clad in snowy mantles,
brooched and gemmed with frosts. Their numbers
I do not care to count, for I know they are the
numbers of my years. The visages of two or three
are sad enough, but on the whole 'tis a congregation of jolly ghosts. The nostrils of my memory
are assailed by a faint odour of plum-pudding and
burnt brandy. I hear a sound as of light music, a
whisk of women's dresses whirled round in dance,
a click as of glasses pledged by friends. Before one
of these apparitions is a mound, as of a new-made
grave, on which the snow is lying. I know, I know!
Drape thyself not in white like the others, but in
mourning stole of crape; and instead of dance
music, let there haunt around thee the service for
the dead! I know that sprig of Mistletoe, O Spirit
in the midst! Under it I swung the girl I loved—
girl no more now than I am boy—and kissed her

spite of blush and pretty shriek. And thou, too, with fragrant trencher in hand, over which blue tongues of flame are playing, do I know—most ancient apparition of them all. I remember thy reigning night. Back to very days of childhood am I taken by thy ghostly raisins simmering in a ghostly brandy flame. Where now the merry boys and girls that thrust their fingers in thy blaze? And now, when I think of it, thee also would I drape in black raiment, around thee also would I make the burial service murmur.

Men hold the anniversaries of their birth, of their marriage, of the birth of their first-born, and they hold—although they spread no feast, and ask no friends to assist—many another anniversary besides. On many a day in every year does a man remember what took place on that self-same day in some former year, and chews the sweet or bitter herb of memory, as the case may be. Could I ever hope to write a decent Essay, I should like to write one "On the Revisiting of Places." It is strange how important the poorest human being is to himself! how he likes to double back on his experiences, to stand on the place he has stood before, to meet himself face to face as it were! I go to the great city in which my early life was spent, and I love to indulge myself in this whim. The only thing I care about is that portion of the city which is connected with myself. I don't think this passion of reminiscence is debased by the slightest taint of vanity. The lamp-post, under the light of which in the winter rain there was a parting so many years ago, I contemplate with the most curious interest. I stare on the windows of the houses in which I once lived, with a feeling which I should find difficult to express in words. I think of the life I led there, of the good and the bad news that came, of the sister who died, of the brother who was born; and were it at all possible, I should like to knock at the once familiar door, and look at the old walls—which could speak to me so strangely—once again. To revisit that city is like walking away back with my yesterdays. I startle myself with myself at the corners of streets, I confront forgotten bits of myself at the entrance to houses. In windows which to another man would seem blank and meaningless, I find personal poems too deep to be ever turned into rhymes—more pathetic, mayhap, than I have ever found on printed page. The spot of ground on which a man has stood is for ever interesting to him. Every experience is an anchor holding him the more firmly to existence. It is for this reason that we hold our sacred days, silent and solitary anniversaries of joy and bitterness, renewing ourselves thereby, going back upon ourselves, living over again the memorable experience. The full yellow moon of next September will gather into itself the light of the full yellow moons of Septembers long ago. In this Christmas night all the other Christmas nights of my life live. How warm, breathing, full of myself is the year 1862, now almost gone! How bare, cheerless, unknown,

the year 1863, about to come in! It stretches before
me in imagination like some great, gaunt un-
tenanted ruin of a Colosseum, in which no footstep
falls, no voice is heard; and by this night year its
naked chambers and windows, three hundred and
sixty-five in number, will be clothed all over, and
hidden by myself as if with covering ivies. Looking
forward into an empty year strikes one with a
certain awe, because one finds therein no recognition. The years behind have a friendly aspect, and
they are warmed by the fires we have kindled, and
all their echoes are the echoes of our own voices.

This, then, is Christmas 1862. Everything is
silent in Dreamthorp. The smith's hammer reposes
beside the anvil. The weaver's flying shuttle is at
rest. Through the clear wintry sunshine the bells
this morning rang from the gray church tower amid
the leafless elms, and up the walk the villagers
trooped in their best dresses and their best faces—
the latter a little reddened by the sharp wind: mere
redness in the middle aged; in the maids, wonderful
bloom to the eyes of their lovers—and took their
places decently in the ancient pews. The clerk read
the beautiful prayers of our Church, which seem
more beautiful at Christmas than at any other
period. For that very feeling which breaks down
at this time the barriers which custom, birth, or
wealth have erected between man and man, strikes
down the barrier of time which intervenes between
the worshipper of to-day and the great body of
worshippers who are at rest in their graves. On

such a day as this, hearing these prayers, we feel
a kinship with the devout generations who heard
them long ago. The devout lips of the Christian
dead murmured the responses which we now murmur; along this road of prayer did their thoughts
of our innumerable dead, our brothers and sisters
in faith and hope, approach the Maker, even as
ours at present approach Him. Prayers over, the
clergyman—who is no Boanerges, or Chrysostom,
golden-mouthed, but a loving, genial-hearted,
pious man, the whole extent of his life from boyhood until now, full of charity and kindly deeds,
as autumn fields with heavy wheaten ears; the
clergyman, I say—for the sentence is becoming
unwieldy on my hands, and one must double back
to secure connexion—read out in that silvery voice
of his, which is sweeter than any music to my ear,
those chapters of the New Testament that deal
with the birth of the Saviour. And the red-faced
rustic congregation hung on the good man's voice
as he spoke of the Infant brought forth in a manger
of the shining angels that appeared in mid-air to
the shepherds, of the miraculous star that took its
station in the sky, and of the wise men who came
from afar and laid their gifts of frankincense and
myrrh at the feet of the Child. With the story every
one was familiar, but on that day, and backed by
the persuasive melody of the reader's voice, it
seemed to all quite new—at least, they listened
attentively as if it were. The discourse that followed possessed no remarkable thoughts; it dealt

simply with the goodness of the Maker of heaven and earth, and the shortness of time, with the duties of thankfulness and charity to the poor; and I am persuaded that every one who heard returned to his house in a better frame of mind. And so the service remitted us all to our own homes, to what roast-beef and plum-pudding slender means permitted, to gatherings around cheerful fires, to half-pleasant, half-sad remembrances of the dead and the absent.

From sermon I have returned like the others, and it is my purpose to hold Christmas alone. I have no one with me at table, and my own thoughts must be my Christmas guests. Sitting here, it is pleasant to think how much kindly feeling exists this present night in England. By imagination I can taste of every table, pledge every toast, silently join in every roar of merriment. I become a sort of universal guest. With what propriety is this jovial season placed amid dismal December rains and snows! How one pities the unhappy Australians, with whom everything is turned topsy-turvy, and who hold Christmas at midsummer! The face of Christmas glows all the brighter for the cold. The heart warms as the frost increases. Estrangements which have embittered the whole year, melt in to-night's hospitable smile. There are warmer hand-shakings on this night than during the by-past twelve months. Friend lives in the mind of friend. There is more charity at this time than at any other. You get up at midnight and toss your spare coppers to the half-benumbed musicians whiffling beneath your windows, although at any other time you would consider their performance a nuisance, and call angrily for the police. Poverty, and scanty clothing, and fireless grates, come home at this season to the bosoms of the rich, and they give of their abundance. The very red-breast of the woods enjoys his Christmas feast. Good feeling incarnates itself in plumpudding. The Master's words, "The poor ye have always with you," wear at this time a deep significance. For at least one night on each year over all Christendom there is brotherhood. And good men, sitting amongst their families, or by a solitary fire like me, when they remember the light that shone over the poor clowns huddling on the Bethlehem plains eighteen hundred years ago, the apparition of shining angels overhead, the song "Peace on earth and goodwill toward men," which for the first time hallowed the midnight air,—pray for that strain's fulfilment, that battle and strife may vex the nations no more, that not only on Christmas-eve, but the whole year round, men shall be brethren, owning one Father in heaven.

Although suggested by the season, and by a solitary dinner, it is not my purpose to indulge in personal reminiscence and talk. Let all that pass. This is Christmas-day, the anniversary of the world's greatest event. To one day all the early world looked forward; to the same day the later world looks back. That day holds time together.

CHRISTMAS

Isaiah, standing on the peaks of prophecy, looked across ruined empires and the desolations of many centuries, and saw on the horizon the new star arise, and was glad. On this night eighteen hundred years ago, Jove was discrowned, the Pagan heaven emptied of its divinities, and Olympus left to the solitude of its snows. On this night, so many hundred years bygone, the despairing voice was heard shrieking on the Aegean, "Pan is dead, great Pan is dead!" On this night, according to the fine reverence of the poets, all things that blast and blight are powerless, disarmed by sweet influences:—

> *Some say that ever 'gainst the season comes*
> *Wherein our Saviour's birth is celebrated*
> *The bird of dawning singeth all night long;*
> *And then they say no spirit dares stir abroad;*
> *The nights are wholesome; then no planets strike;*
> *No fairy takes, nor witch hath power to charm:*
> *So hallow'd and so gracious is the time.*

The flight of the pagan mythology before the new faith has been a favourite subject with the poets; and it has been my custom for many seasons to read Milton's "Hymn to the Nativity" on the evening of Christmas Day. The bass of heaven's deep organ seems to blow in the lines, and slowly and with many echoes the strain melts into silence. To my ear the lines sound like the full-voiced choir and the rolling organ of a cathedral, when the afternoon light streaming through the painted

windows fills the place with solemn colours and
masses of gorgeous gloom. To-night I shall float
my lonely hours away on music:—

> *The oracles are dumb,*
> *No voice or hideous hum*
> *Runs through the archèd roof in words deceiving:*
> *Apollo from his shrine*
> *Can no more divine*
> *With hollow shriek the steep of Delphos leaving.*
> *No nightly trance or breathèd spell*
> *Inspires the pale-eyed priest from the prophetic cell.*

> *The lonely mountains o'er,*
> *And the resounding shore,*
> *A voice of weeping heard and loud lament:*
> *From haunted spring, and dale*
> *Edged with poplars pale,*
> *The parting genius is with sighing sent:*
> *With flower-enwoven tresses torn*
> *The nymphs in twilight shades of tangled thickets*
> *mourn.*

> *Peor and Baalim*
> *Forsake their temples dim*
> *With that twice-batter'd god of Palestine;*
> *And moonèd Ashtaroth,*
> *Heaven's queen and mother both,*
> *Now sits not girt with tapers' holy shine!*
> *The Lybic Hammon shrinks his horn,*
> *In vain the Tyrian maids their wounded Thammuz*
> *mourn.*

And sullen Moloch, fled,
Hath left in shadows dread
His burning idol, all of blackest hue:
In vain with cymbals' ring
They call the grisly king
In dismal dance about the furnace blue:
The brutish gods of Nile as fast,
Isis, and Orus, and the dog Anubis haste.

He feels from Juda's land
The dreaded Infant's hand,
The rays of Bethlehem blind his dusky eyne:
Nor all the gods beside
Dare longer there abide,
Not Typhon huge ending in snaky twine.
Our Babe to shew His Godhead true
Can in His swaddling bands control the damnèd
crew.

These verses, as if loath to die, linger with a
certain persistence in mind and ear. This is the
"mighty line" which critics talk about! And just
as in an infant's face you may discern the rudi-
ments of the future man, so in the glorious hymn
may be traced the more majestic lineaments of the
"Paradise Lost."

Strangely enough, the next noblest dirge for the
unrealmed divinities which I can call to remembrance, and at the same time the most eloquent
celebration of the new power and prophecy of its
triumph, has been uttered by Shelley, who cannot

in any sense be termed a Christian poet. It is one
of the choruses in "Hellas," and perhaps had he
lived longer amongst us, it would have been the
prelude to higher strains. Of this I am certain, that
before his death the mind of that brilliant genius
was rapidly changing—that for him the Cross was
gathering attractions round it—that the wall which
he complained had been built up between his heart
and his intellect was being broken down, and that
rays of a strange splendour were already streaming
upon him through the interstices. What a contrast
between the darkened glory of "Queen Mab"—of
which in after-life he was ashamed, both as a
literary work and as an expression of opinion—and
the intense, clear, lyrical light of this triumphant
poem!—

> *A power from the unknown God,*
>   *A Promethean conqueror came:*
> *Like a triumphal path he trod*
>   *The thorns of death and shame.*
>   *A mortal shape to him*
>   *Was like the vapour dim*
> *Which the orient planet animates with light.*
>   *Hell, sin, and slavery came*
>   *Like bloodhounds mild and tame,*
> *Nor prey'd until their lord had taken flight.*
>   *The moon of Mahomet*
>   *Arose, and it shall set;*
> *While blazon'd, as on heaven's immortal noon,*
>   *The Cross leads generations on.*

Swift as the radiant shapes of sleep,
  From one whose dreams are paradise,
Fly, when the fond wretch wakes to weep,
  And day peers forth with her blank eyes:
    So fleet, so faint, so fair,
    The powers of earth and air
Fled from the folding-star of Bethlehem.
    Apollo, Pan, and Love,
    And even Olympian Jove,
Grew weak, for killing Truth had glared on them.
    Our hills, and seas, and streams,
    Dispeopled of their dreams,
Their waters turn'd to blood, their dew to tears,
  Wail'd for the golden years.

For my own part, I cannot read these lines without emotion—not so much for their beauty as for the change in the writer's mind which they suggest. The self-sacrifice which lies at the centre of Christianity should have touched this man more deeply than almost any other. That it was beginning to touch and mould him, I verily believe. He died and made *that* sign. Of what music did that storm in Spezia Bay rob the world!

"The Cross leads generations on." Believing as I do that my own personal decease is not more certain than that our religion will subdue the world, I own that it is with a somewhat saddened heart that I pass my thoughts around the globe, and consider how distant is yet that triumph. There are the realms on which the Crescent beams, the monstrous many-headed gods of India, the Chinaman's heathenism, the African's devil-rites. These are, to a large extent, principalities and powers of darkness with which our religion has never been brought into collision, save at trivial and far-separated points, and in these cases the attack has never been made in strength. But what of our own Europe—the home of philosophy, of poetry, and painting? Europe, which has produced Greece, and Rome, and England's centuries of glory; which has been illumined by the fires of martyrdom; which has heard a Luther preach; which has listened to Dante's "mystic unfathomable song"; to which Milton has opened the door of heaven—what of it? And what, too, of that younger America, starting in its career with all our good things, and enfranchised of many of our evils? Did not the December sun now shining look down on thousands slaughtered at Fredricksburg, in a most mad, most incomprehensible quarrel? And is not the public air which European nations breathe at this moment, as it has been for several years back, charged with thunder? Despots are plotting, ships are building, man's ingenuity is bent, as it never was bent before, on the invention and improvement of instruments of death; Europe is bristling with five millions of bayonets: and this is the condition of a world for which the Son of God died eighteen hundred and sixty-two years ago! There is no mystery of Providence so inscrutable as this; and yet, is not the very sense of its mournfulness a proof that the spirit of Christianity is living in the minds of men? For, of a verity, military glory is becoming in our best thoughts a bloody rag, and conquest the first in the catalogue of mighty crimes, and a throned tyrant, with armies, and treasures, and the cheers of millions rising up like a cloud of incense around him, but a mark for the thunderbolt of Almighty God—in reality poorer than Lazarus stretched at the gate of Dives. Besides, all these things are getting themselves to some extent mitigated. Florence Nightingale—for the first time in the history of the world —walks through the Scutari hospitals, and "poor, noble, wounded, and sick men," to use her Majesty's tender phrases, kiss her shadow as it falls on them. The Emperor Napoleon does not make war to employ his armies, or to consolidate his power; he does so for the sake of an "idea" more or less generous and disinterested. The soul of mankind would revolt at the blunt, naked truth; and the taciturn emperor knows this, as he knows most things. This imperial hypocrisy, like every other hypocrisy, is a homage which vice pays to virtue. There cannot be a doubt that when the political crimes of kings and governments, the sores that fester in the heart of society, and all "the burden of the unintelligible world," weigh heaviest on the mind, we have to thank Christianity for it. That pure light makes visible the darkness. The Sermon on the Mount makes the morality of the nations ghastly. The Divine love makes human hate stand out in dark relief. This sadness, in the essence of it nobler than any joy, is the heritage of the Christian. An ancient Roman could not have felt so. Everything runs on smoothly enough so long as Jove wields the thunder. But Venus, Mars, and Minerva are far behind us now; the Cross is before us; and self-denial and sorrow for sin, and the remembrance of the poor, and the cleansing of our own hearts, are duties incumbent upon every one of us. If the Christian is less happy than the pagan, and at times I think he is so, it arises from the reproach of the Christian's unreached ideal, and from the stings of his finer and more scrupulous conscience. His whole moral organisation is finer, and he must pay the noble penalty of finer organisations.

Once again, for the purpose of taking away all solitariness of feeling, and of connecting myself, albeit only in fancy, with the proper gladness of the time, let me think of the comfortable family dinners now being drawn to a close, of the good wishes uttered, and the presents made, quite valueless in themselves, yet felt to be invaluable from the feelings from which they spring; of the little children, by sweetmeats lapped in Elysium; and of the pantomime, pleasantest Christmas sight of all, with the pit a sea of grinning delight, the boxes a tier of beaming juvenility, the galleries, piled up to the far-receding roof, a mass of happy laughter which a clown's joke brings down in mighty avalanches. In the pit, sober people relax themselves, and suck oranges, and quaff ginger-pop; in the boxes, Miss, gazing through her curls, thinks the Fairy Prince the prettiest creature she ever beheld, and Master, that to be a clown must be the pinnacle of human happiness; while up in the galleries the hard literal world is for an hour sponged out and obliterated; the chimney-sweep forgets, in his delight when the policeman comes to grief, the harsh call of his master, and Cinderella, when the demons are foiled, and the long-parted lovers meet and embrace in a paradise of light and pink gauze, the grates that must be scrubbed to-morrow. All bands and trappings of toil are for one hour loosened by the hands of imaginative sympathy. What happiness a single theatre can contain! And those of maturer years, or of more meditative temperament, sitting at the pantomime, can extract out of the shifting scenes meanings suitable to themselves; for the pantomime is a symbol or adumbration of human life. Have we not all known Harlequin, who rules the roast, and has the pretty Columbine to himself? Do we not all know that rogue of a clown with his peculating fingers, who brazens out of every scrape, and who conquers the world by good humour and ready wit? And have we not seen Pantaloons not a few, whose fate it is to get all the kicks and lose all the half-pence, to fall through all the trap-doors, break their shins over all the barrows, and be for ever captured by the policeman, while the true pilferer, the clown, makes his escape with the booty in his possession?

Methinks I know the realities of which these things
are but the shadows; have met with them in business, have sat with them at dinner. But to-night no
such notions as these intrude; and when the torrent
of fun, and transformation, and practical joking
which rushed out of the beautiful fairy world, is in
the beautiful fairy world gathered up again, the
high-heaped happiness of the theatre will disperse
itself, and the Christmas pantomime will be a
pleasant memory the whole year through. Thousands on thousands of people are having their
midriffs tickled at this moment; in fancy I see their
lighted faces, in memory I hear their mirth.

By this time I should think every Christmas
dinner at Dreamthorp or elsewhere has come to an
end. Even now in the great cities the theatres will
be dispersing. The clown has wiped the paint off his
face. Harlequin has laid aside his wand, and di-
vested himself of his glittering raiment; Pantaloon,
after refreshing himself with a pint of porter, is
rubbing his aching joints; and Columbine, wrapped
up in a shawl, and with sleepy eyelids, has gone
home in a cab. Soon, in the great theatre, the lights
will be put out, and the empty stage will be left to
ghosts. Hark! midnight from the church tower
vibrates through the frosty air. I look out on the
brilliant heaven, and see a milky way of powdery
splendour wandering through it, and clusters and
knots of stars and planets shining serenely in the
blue frosty spaces; and the armed apparition of
Orion, his spear pointing away into immeasurable

space, gleaming overhead; and the familiar con-
stellation of the Plough dipping down into the
west; and I think when I go in again that there
is one Christmas the less between me and my
grave.

MEN OF LETTERS

MR. HAZLITT has written many pleasant essays, but none pleasanter than that entitled "My First Acquaintance with Poets," which, in the edition edited by his son, opens the *Winterslow* series. It relates almost entirely to Coleridge; containing sketches of his personal appearance, fragments of his conversation, and is filled with a young man's generous enthusiasm, belief, admiration, as with sunrise. He had met Coleridge, walked with him, talked with him, and the high intellectual experience not only made him better acquainted with his own spirit and its folded powers, but—as is ever the case with such spiritual encounters—it touched and illuminated the dead outer world. The road between Wem and Shrewsbury was familiar enough to Hazlitt, but as the twain passed along it on that winter day, it became etherialised, poetic—wonderful, as if leading across the Delectable Mountains to the Golden City, whose gleam is discernible on the horizon. The milestones were mute with attention, the pines upon the hill had ears for the stranger as he passed.

Eloquence made the red leaves rustle on the oak; made the depth of heaven seem as if swept by a breath of spring; and when the evening star appeared, Hazlitt saw it as Adam did while in Paradise and but one day old. "As we passed along," writes the essayist, "between Wem and Shrewsbury, and I eyed the blue hill tops seen through the wintry branches, or the red, rustling leaves of the sturdy oak-trees by the wayside, a sound was in my ears as of a syren's song. I was stunned, startled with it as from deep sleep; but I had no notion that I should ever be able to express my admiration to others in motley imagery or quaint allusion, till the light of his genius shone into my soul, like the sun's rays glittering in the puddles of the road. I was at that time dumb, inarticulate, helpless, like a worm by the wayside, crushed, bleeding, lifeless; but now, bursting from the deadly bands that bound them, my ideas float on winged words, and as they expand their plumes, catch the golden light of other years. My soul has indeed remained in its original bondage, dark, obscure, with longings infinite and unsatisfied; my heart, shut up in the prison-house of this rude clay, has never found, nor will it ever find, a heart to speak to; but that my understanding also did not remain dumb and brutish, or at length found a language to express itself, I owe to Coleridge." Time and sorrow, personal ambition thwarted and fruitlessly driven back on itself, hopes for the world defeated and unrealised, changed the en-

thusiastic youth into a petulant, unsocial man;
yet ever as he remembered that meeting and his
wintry walk from Wem to Shrewsbury the early
glow came back, and again a "sound was in his ears
as of a syren's song."

We are not all hero-worshippers like Hazlitt,
but most of us are so to a large extent. A large
proportion of mankind feel a quite peculiar interest
in famous writers. They like to read about them,
to know what they said on this or the other occasion, what sort of house they inhabited, what
fashion of dress they wore, if they liked any
particular dish for dinner, what kind of women
they fell in love with, and whether their domestic
atmosphere was stormy or the reverse. Concerning
such men no bit of information is too trifling;
everything helps to make out the mental image
we have dimly formed for ourselves. And this kind
of interest is heightened by the artistic way in
which time occasionally groups them. The race is
gregarious; they are visible to us in clumps like
primroses; they are brought into neighbourhood
and flash light on each other like gems in a diadem.
We think of the wild geniuses who came up from
the universities to London in the dawn of the English drama. Greene, Nash, Marlowe—our first
professional men of letters—how they cracked
their satirical whips, how they brawled in taverns,
how pinched they were at times, how, when they
possessed money, they flung it from them as if it
were poison, with what fierce speed they wrote,

how they shook the stage. Then we think of the "Mermaid" in session, with Shakspeare's bland, oval face, the light of a smile spread over it, and Ben Jonson's truculent visage, and Beaumont and Fletcher sitting together in their beautiful friend-ship, and fancy as best we can the drollery, the repartee, the sage sentences, the lightning gleams of wit, the thunder-peals of laughter.

> *What things have we seen*
> *Done at the Mermaid! Heard words that have been*
> *So nimble, and so full of subtle flame,*
> *As if that every one from whence they came*
> *Had meant to put his whole soul in a jest,*
> *And had resolved to live a fool the rest*
> *Of his dull life.*

Then there is the "Literary Club," with Johnson, and Garrick, and Burke, and Reynolds, and Gold-smith sitting in perpetuity in Boswell. The Doctor has been talking there for a hundred years, and there will he talk for many a hundred more. And we of another generation, and with other things to think about, can enter any night we please, and hear what is going on. Then we have the swarthy ploughman from Ayrshire sitting at Lord Mon-boddo's with Dr. Blair, Dugald Stewart, Henry Mackenzie, and the rest. These went into the presence of the wonderful rustic thoughtlessly enough, and now they cannot return even if they would. They are defrauded of oblivion. Not yet have they tasted forgetfulness and the grave. The day may come when Burns shall be forgotten, but till that day arrives—and the eastern sky as yet gives no token of its approach—*him* they must attend as satellites the sun, as courtiers their king. Then there are the Lakers—Wordsworth, Coleridge, Southey, De Quincey burdened with his tremendous dream, Wilson in his splendid youth. What talk, what argument, what readings of lyrical and other ballads, what contempt of critics, what a hail of fine things! Then there is Charles Lamb's room in Inner Temple Lane, the hush of a whist table in one corner, the host stuttering puns as he deals the cards; and sitting round about, Hunt, whose every sentence is flavoured with the hawthorn and the primrose, and Hazlitt maddened by Waterloo and St. Helena, and Godwin with his wild theories, and Kemble with his Roman look. And before the morning comes, and Lamb stutters yet more thickly—for there is a slight flavour of punch in the apartment—what talk there has been of Hogarth's prints, of Izaak Walton, of the old dramatists, of Sir Thomas Browne's "Urn Burial," with Elia's quaint humour breaking through every interstice, and flowering in every fissure and cranny of the conversation! One likes to think of these social gatherings of wits and geniuses; they are more interesting than conclaves of kings or convocations of bishops. One would like to have been the waiter at the "Mermaid," and to have stood behind Shakspeare's chair. What was that functionary's opinion of his guests? Did he listen and become witty by infection? or did he, when his task was over, retire unconcernedly to chalk up the tavern score? One envies somewhat the damsel who brought Lamb the spirit-case and the hot water. I think of these meetings, and, in lack of companionship, frame for myself imaginary conversations—not so brilliant, of course, as Mr. Landor's, but yet sufficient to make pleasant for me the twilight hour while the lamp is yet unlit, and my solitary room is filled with the ruddy lights and shadows of the fire.

Of human notabilities men of letters are the most interesting, and this arises mainly from their outspokenness as a class. The writer makes himself known in a way that no other man makes himself known. The distinguished engineer may be as great a man as the distinguished writer, but as a rule we know little about him. We see him invent a locomotive, or bridge a strait, but there our knowledge stops; we look at the engine, we walk across the bridge, we admire the ingenuity of the one, we are grateful for the conveniency of the other, but to our apprehensions the engineer is undeciphered all the while. Doubtless he reveals himself in his work as the poet reveals himself in his song, but then this revelation is made in a tongue unknown to the majority. After all, we do not feel that we get nearer him. The man of letters, on the other hand, is outspoken, he takes you into his confidence, he keeps no secret

from you. Be you beggar, be you king, you are
welcome. He is no respecter of persons. He gives
without reserve his fancies, his wit, his wisdom;
he makes you a present of all that the painful
or the happy years have brought him. The writer
makes his reader heir in full. Men of letters are
a peculiar class. They are never commonplace
or prosaic—at least those of them that mankind
care for. They are airy, wise, gloomy, melodious
spirits. They give us the language we speak,
they furnish the subjects of our best talk. They
are full of generous impulses and sentiments, and
keep the world young. They have said fine things
on every phase of human experience. The air is
full of their voices. Their books are the world's
holiday and playground, and into these neither
care, nor the dun, nor despondency can follow
the enfranchised man. Men of letters forerun science as the morning star the dawn. Nothing has
been invented, nothing has been achieved, but
has gleamed a bright-coloured Utopia in the eyes
of one or the other of these men. Several centuries
before the Great Exhibition of 1851 rose in Hyde
Park, a wondrous hall of glass stood, radiant in
sunlight, in the verse of Chaucer. The electric
telegraph is not so swift as the flight of Puck.
We have not yet realised the hippogriff of Ariosto.
Just consider what a world this would be if ruled
by the best thoughts of men of letters! Ignorance
would die at once, war would cease, taxation would
be lightened, not only every Frenchman, but

every man in the world, would have his hen in the pot. May would not marry January. The race of lawyers and physicians would be extinct. Fancy a world, the affairs of which are directed by Goethe's wisdom and Goldsmith's heart! In such a case methinks the millennium were already come. Books are a finer world within the world. With books are connected all my desires and aspirations. When I go to my long sleep, on a book will my head be pillowed. I care for no other fashion of greatness. I'd as lief not be remembered at all as remembered in connexion with anything else. I would rather be Charles Lamb than Charles XII. I would rather be remembered by a song than by a victory. I would rather build a fine sonnet than have built St. Paul's. I would rather be the discoverer of a new image than the discoverer of a new planet. Fine phrases I value more than bank-notes. I have ear for no other harmony than the harmony of words. To be occasionally quoted is the only fame I care for.

But what of the literary life? How fares it with the men whose days and nights are devoted to the writing of books? We know the famous men of letters, we give them the highest place in our regards; we crown them with laurels so thickly that we hide the furrows on their foreheads. Yet we must remember that there are men of letters who have been equally sanguine, equally ardent, who have pursued perfection equally unselfishly, but who have failed to make themselves famous.

We know the ships that come with streaming pennons into the immortal ports; we know but little of the ships that have gone on fire on the way thither—that have gone down at sea. Even with successful men we cannot know precisely how matters have gone. We read the fine raptures of the poet, but we do not know into what kind of being he relapses when the inspiration is over, any more than, seeing and hearing the lark shrilling at the gate of heaven, we know with what effort it has climbed thither, or into what kind of nest it must descend. The lark is not always singing; no more is the poet. The lark is only interesting *while* singing, at other times it is but a plain brown bird. We may not be able to recognise the poet when he doffs his singing robes; he may then sink to the level of his admirers. We laugh at the fancies of the humorist, but he may have written his brilliant things in a dismal enough mood. The writer is not continually dwelling amongst the roses and lilies of life, he is not continually uttering generous sentiments, and saying fine things. On him, as on his brethren, the world presses with its prosaic needs. He has to make love and marry, and run the usual matrimonial risks. The income-tax collector visits him as well as others. Around his head at Christmas-times drives a snowstorm of bills. He must keep the wolf from the door, and he has only his goose-quills to confront it with. And here it is, having to deal with alien powers, that his special temperament comes into play, and may work him evil. Wit is not worldly wisdom. A man gazing on the stars is proverbially at the mercy of the puddles on the road. A man may be able to disentangle intricate problems, be able to recall the past, and yet be cozened by an ordinary knave. The finest expression will not liquidate a butcher's account. If Apollo puts his name to a bill, he must meet it when it becomes due, or go into the *Gazette*. Armies are not always cheering on the heights which they have won; there are forced marches, occasional shortness of provisions, bivouacs on muddy plains, driving in of pickets, and the like, although these inglorious items are forgotten when we read the roll of victories inscribed on their banners. The books of the great writer are only portions of the great writer. His life acts on his writings; his writings react on his life. His life may impoverish his books; his books may impoverish his life. Apollo's

Branch that might have grown full straight,

may have the worm of a vulgar misery gnawing at its roots. The heat of inspiration may be subtracted from the household fire; and those who sit by it may be the colder in consequence. A man may put all his good things in his books, and leave none for his life, just as a man may expend his fortune on a splendid dress, and carry a pang of hunger beneath it.

There are few less exhilarating books than the

biographies of men of letters, and of artists generally; and this arises from the pictures of comparative defeat which, in almost every instance, such books contain. In these books we see failure more or less—seldom clear, victorious effort. If the art is exquisite, the marble is flawed; if the marble is pure, there is defect in art. There is always something lacking in the poem; there is always irremediable defect in the picture. In the biography we see persistent, passionate effort, and almost constant repulse. If, on the whole, victory is gained, one wing of the army has been thrown into confusion. In the life of a successful farmer, for instance, one feels nothing of this kind; his year flows on harmoniously, fortunately: through ploughing, seed-time, growth of grain, the yellowing of it beneath meek autumn suns and big autumn moons, the cutting of it down, riotous harvest-home, final sale, and large balance at the banker's. From the point of view of almost unvarying success the farmer's life becomes beautiful, poetic. Everything is an aid and help to him. Nature puts her shoulder to his wheel. He takes the winds, the clouds, the sunbeams, the rolling stars into partnership, and, asking no dividend, they let him retain the entire profits. As a rule, the lives of men of letters do not flow on in this successful way. In their case there is always either defect in the soil or defect in the husbandry. Like the Old Guard at Waterloo, they are fighting bravely on a lost field. In literary biography there is always an element of tragedy, and the love we bear the dead is mingled with pity. Of course the life of a man of letters is more perilous than the life of a farmer; more perilous than almost any other kind of life which it is given a human being to conduct. It is more difficult to obtain the mastery over spiritual ways and means than over material ones, and he must command *both*. Properly to conduct his life he must not only take large crops off his fields, he must also leave in his fields the capacity of producing large crops. It is easy to drive in your chariot two horses of one breed; not so easy when the one is of terrestrial stock, the other of celestial; in every respect different—in colour, temper, and pace.

At the outset of his career, the man of letters is confronted by the fact that he must live. The obtaining of a livelihood is preliminary to everything else. Poets and cobblers are placed on the same level so far. If the writer can barter MSS. for sufficient coin, he may proceed to develop himself; if he cannot so barter it, there is a speedy end of himself, and of his development also. Literature has become a profession; but it is in several respects different from the professions by which other human beings earn their bread. The man of letters, unlike the clergyman, the physician, or the lawyer, has to undergo no special preliminary training for his work, and while engaged in it, unlike the professional persons named, he has no accredited status. Of course, to earn any success, he must start with as much special knowledge, with as much dexterity in his craft, as your ordinary physician; but then he is not recognised till once he is successful. When a man takes a physician's degree, he has done something; when a man betakes himself to literary pursuits, he has done nothing—till once he is lucky enough to make his mark. There is no special preliminary training for men of letters, and, as a consequence, their ranks are recruited from the vagrant talent of the world. Men that break loose from the professions, who stray from the beaten tracks of life, take refuge in literature. In it are to be found doctors, lawyers, clergymen, and the motley nation of Bohemians. Any one possessed of a nimble brain, a quire of paper, a steel pen, and ink-bottle, can start business. Any one who chooses may enter the lists, and no questions are asked concerning his antecedents. The battle is won by sheer strength of brain. From all this it comes that the man of letters has usually a history of his own: his individuality is more pronounced than the individuality of other men; he has been knocked about by passion and circumstance. All his life he has had a dislike for iron rules and commonplace maxims. There is something of the gipsy in his nature. He is to some extent eccentric, and he indulges his eccentricity. And the misfortunes of men of letters—the vulgar and patent misfortunes, I mean—arise mainly from the want of harmony between their impulsiveness and volatility, and the staid unmercurial world with which they are brought into conflict. They are unconventional in a world of conventions; they are fanciful, and are constantly misunderstood in prosaic relations. They are wise enough in their books, for there they are sovereigns, and can shape everything to their own likings; out of their books, they are not unfrequently extremely foolish, for they exist then in the territory of an alien power, and are constantly knocking their heads against existing orders of things. Men of letters take prosaic men out of themselves; but they are weak where the prosaic men are strong. They have their own way in the world of ideas, prosaic men in the world of facts. From his practical errors the writer learns something, if not always humility and amendment. A memorial flower grows on every spot where he has come to grief; and the chasm he cannot over-leap he bridges with a rainbow.

But the man of letters has not only to live, he has to develop himself; and his earning of money and his intellectual development should proceed simultaneously and in proportionate degrees. Herein lies the main difficulty of the literary life. Out of his thought the man must bring fire, food, clothing; and fire, food, clothing must in their turns subserve thought. It is necessary, for the proper conduct of such a life, that while the balance at the banker's increases, intellectual resource should increase at the same ratio. Progress should not be made in the faculty of expression alone—progress at the same time should be made in thought; for thought is the material on which expression feeds. Should sufficient advance not be made in this last direction, in a short time the man feels that he has expressed himself—that now he can only more or less dexterously repeat himself—more or less prettily become his own echo. It is comparatively easy to acquire facility in writing; but it is an evil thing for the man of letters when such facility is the only thing he has acquired—when it has been, perhaps, the only thing he has striven to acquire. Such miscalculation of ways and means suggests vulgarity of aspiration, and a fatal material taint. In the life in which this error has been committed there can be no proper harmony, no satisfaction, no spontaneous delight in effort. The man does not create —he is only desperately keeping up appearances. He has at once become "a base mechanical," and his successes are not much higher than the successes of the acrobat or the rope-dancer. This want of proper relationship between resources of expression and resources of thought, or subject-matter for expression, is common enough, and some slight suspicion of it flashes across the mind at times in reading even the best authors. It lies at the bottom of every catastrophe in the literary life. Frequently a man's first book is good, and all his after productions but faint and yet fainter reverberations of the first. The men who act thus are in the long run deserted like worked-out mines. A man reaches his limits as to thought long before he reaches his limits as to expression; and a haunting suspicion of this is one of the peculiar bitters of the literary life. Hazlitt tells us that, after one of his early interviews with Coleridge, he sat down to his Essay on the Natural Disinterestedness of the Human Mind. "I sat down to the task shortly afterwards for the twentieth time, got new pens and paper, determined to make clean work of it, wrote a few sentences in the skeleton style of a mathematical demonstration, stopped half-way down the second page, and, after trying in vain to pump up any words, images, notions, apprehensions, facts, or observations, from that gulf of abstraction in which I had plunged myself for four or five years preceding, gave up the attempt as labour in vain, and shed tears of hopeless despondency on the blank unfinished paper. I can write fast enough now. Am I better than I was then? oh no! One truth discovered, one pang of regret at not being able to express it, is worth all the fluency and flippancy in the world." This regretful looking back to the past, when emotions were keen and sharp, and when thought wore the novel dress of a stranger, and this dissatisfaction with the acquirements of the present, is common enough with the man of letters. The years have come and gone, and he is conscious that he is not intrinsically richer—he has only learned to assort and display his riches to advantage. His wares have neither increased in quantity nor improved in quality—he has only procured a window in a leading thoroughfare. He can catch his butterflies more cunningly, he can pin them on his cards more skilfully, but their wings are fingered and tawdry compared with the time when they winnowed before him in the sunshine over the meadows of youth. This species of regret is peculiar to the class of which I am speaking, and they often discern failure in what the world counts success. The veteran does not look back to the time when he was in the awkward squad; the accountant does not sigh over the time when he was bewildered by the mysteries of double-entry. And the reason is obvious. The dexterity which time and practice have brought to the soldier and the accountant is pure gain: the dexterity of expression which time and practice have brought to the writer is gain too, in its way, but not quite so pure. It may have been cultivated and brought to its degree of excellence at the expense of higher things. The man of letters lives by thought and expression, and his two powers may not be perfectly balanced. And, putting aside its effect on the reader, and through that, on the writer's pecuniary prosperity, the tragedy of want of equipoise lies in this. When the writer expresses his thought, it is immediately dead to him, however life-giving it may be to others; he pauses midway in his career, he looks back over his uttered past—brown desert to him, in which there is no sustenance—he looks forward to the green *un*uttered future, and beholding its narrow limits, knows it is all that he can call his own—on that vivid strip he must pasture his intellectual life.

Is the literary life, on the whole, a happy one? Granted that the writer is productive, that he possesses abundance of material, that he has secured the ear of the world, one is inclined to fancy that no life could be happier. Such a man seems to live on the finest of the wheat. If a poet, he is continually singing; if a novelist, he is supreme in his ideal world; if a humorist, everything smiles back upon his smile; if an essayist, he is continually saying the wisest, most memorable things. He breathes habitually the serener air which ordinary mortals can only at intervals respire, and in their happiest moments. Such conceptions of great writers are to some extent erroneous. Through the medium of their books we know them only in their active mental states—in their triumphs; we do not see them when sluggishness has succeeded the effort which was delight. The statue does not come to her white limbs all at once. It is the bronze wrestler, not the flesh-and-blood one, that stands for ever over a fallen adversary with the pride of victory on his face. Of the labour, the weariness, the self-distrust, the utter despondency of the great writer, we know nothing. Then, for the attainment of mere happiness or contentment, any high faculty of imagination is a questionable help. Of course imagination lights the torch of joy, it deepens the carmine on the sleek cheek of the girl, it makes wine sparkle, makes music speak, gives rays to the rising sun. But in all its supreme sweetnesses there is a perilous admixture of deceit, which is suspected even at the moment when the senses tingle keenliest. And it must be remembered that this potent faculty can darken as well as brighten. It is the very soul of pain. While the trumpets are blowing in Ambition's ear, it whispers of the grave. It drapes Death in austere solemnities, and surrounds him with a gloomy court of terrors. The life of the imaginative man is never a commonplace one: his lights are brighter, his glooms are darker, than the lights and glooms of the vulgar. His ecstasies are as restless as his pains. The great writer has this perilous faculty in excess; and through it he will, as a matter of course, draw out of the atmosphere of circumstance surrounding the keenness of pleasure and pain. To my own notion, the best gifts of the gods are neither the most glittering nor the most admired. These gifts I take to be, a moderate ambition, a taste for repose with circumstances favourable thereto, a certain mildness of passion, an even-beating pulse, an even-beating heart. I do not consider heroes and celebrated persons the happiest of mankind. I do not envy Alexander the shouting of his armies, nor Dante his laurel wreath. Even were I able, I would not purchase these at the prices the poet and the warrior paid. So far, then, as great writers—great poets, especially—are of imagination all compact—a peculiarity of mental constitution which makes a man go shares with every one he is brought into contact with; which makes him enter into Romeo's rapture when he touches Juliet's cheek among cypresses silvered by the Verona moonlight, and the stupor of the blinded and pinioned wretch on the scaffold before the bolt is drawn—so far as this special gift goes, I do not think the great poet—and by virtue of it he *is* a poet—is likely to be happier than your more ordinary mortal. On the whole, perhaps, it is the great readers rather than the great writers who are entirely to be envied. They pluck the fruits, and are spared the trouble of rearing them. Prometheus filched fire from heaven, and had for reward the crag of Caucasus, the chain, the vulture; while they for whom he stole it cook their suppers upon it, stretch out benumbed hands towards it, and see its light reflected in their children's faces. They are comfortable: he, roofed by the keen crystals of the stars, groans above.

Trifles make up the happiness or the misery of mortal life. The majority of men slip into their graves without having encountered on their way thither any signal catastrophe or exaltation of fortune or feeling. Collect a thousand ignited sticks into a heap, and you have a bonfire which may be seen over three counties. If, during thirty years, the annoyances connected with shirt-buttons found missing when you are hurriedly dressing for dinner, were gathered into a mass and endured at once, it would be misery equal to a public execution. If, from the same space of time, all the little titillations of a man's vanity were gathered into one lump of honey and enjoyed at once, the pleasure of being crowned would not perhaps be much greater. If the equanimity of an ordinary man be at the mercy of trifles, how much more will the equanimity of the man of letters, who is usually the most sensitive of the race, and whose peculiar avocation makes sad work with the fine tissues of the nerves. Literary composition is, I take it, with the exception of the crank, in which there is neither hope nor result, the most exhausting to which a human being can apply himself. Just consider the situation. Here is your man of letters, tender-hearted as Cowper, who would not count upon his list of friends the man who tramples heedlessly upon a worm; as light of sleep and abhorrent of noise as Beattie, who denounces chanticleer for his lusty proclamation of morning to his own and the neighbouring farmyards in terms that would be unmeasured if applied to Nero; as alive to blame as Byron, who declared that the praise of the greatest of the race could not take the sting from the censure of the meanest. Fancy the sufferings of a creature so built and strung in a world which creaks so vilely on its hinges as this! Will such a man confront a dun with an imperturbable countenance? Will he throw himself back in his chair and smile blandly when his chamber is lanced through and through by the notes of a street bagpiper? When his harassed brain should be solaced by music, will he listen patiently to stupid remarks? I fear not. The man of letters suffers keenlier than people suspect from sharp, cruel noises, from witless observations, from social misconceptions of him of every kind, from hard utilitarian wisdom, and from his own good things going to the grave unrecognised and unhonoured. And, forced to live by his pen, to extract from his brain bread and beer, clothing, lodging, and income tax, I am not surprised that he is oftentimes nervous, querulous, impatient. Thinking of these things, I do not wonder at Hazlitt's spleen, at Charles Lamb's punch, at Coleridge's opium. I think of the days spent in writing, and of the nights which repeat the day in dream, and in which there is no refreshment. I think of the brain which must be worked out at length: of Scott, when the wand of the enchanter was broken, writing poor romances; of Southey sitting vacantly in his library, and drawing a feeble satisfaction from the faces of his books. And for the man of letters there is more than the mere labour: he writes his book, and has frequently the mortification of seeing it neglected or torn to pieces. Above all men, he longs for sympathy, recognition, applause. He respects his fellow-creature, because he beholds in him a possible reader. To write a book, to send it forth to the world and the critics, is to a sensi-

tive person like plunging mother-naked into tropic
waters where sharks abound. It is true that, like
death, the terror of criticism lives most in apprehension; still, to have been frequently criticised,
and to be constantly liable to it, are disagreeable
items in a man's life. Most men endure criticism
with commendable fortitude, just as most criminals when under the drop conduct themselves
with calmness. They bleed, but they bleed inwardly. To be flayed in the *Saturday Review*, for
instance—a whole amused public looking on—is
far from pleasant; and, after the operation, the
ordinary annoyances of life probably magnify
themselves into tortures. The grasshopper becomes a burden. Touch a flayed man ever so
lightly, and with ever so kindly an intention, and
he is sure to wince. The skin of the man of letters
is peculiarly sensitive to the bite of the critical
mosquito; and he lives in a climate in which such
mosquitoes swarm. He is seldom stabbed to the
heart—he is often killed by pin-pricks.

But, to leave palisade and outwork, and come
to the interior of the citadel, it may be said that
great writers, although they must ever remain
shining objects of regard to us, are not exempted
from ordinary limitations and conditions. They
are cabined, cribbed, confined, even as their more
prosaic brethren. It is in the nature of every man
to be endued with that he works in. Thus, in
course of time, the merchant becomes bound up
in his ventures and his ledger; an indefinable

flavour of the pharmacopoeia lingers about the physician; the bombazin and horsehair of the lawyer eat into his soul—his experiences are docqueted in a clerkly hand, bound together with red tape, and put away in professional pigeon-holes. A man naturally becomes leavened by the profession which he has adopted. He thinks, speaks, and dreams "shop," as the colloquial phrase has it. Men of letters are affected by their profession just as merchants, physicians, and lawyers are. In course of time the inner man becomes stained with ink, like blotting-paper. The agriculturist talks constantly of bullocks—the man of letters constantly of books. The printing-press seems constantly in his immediate neigh-bourhood. He is stretched on the rack of an un-favourable review—he is lapped in the Elysium of a new edition. The narrowing effect of a profes-sion is in every man a defect, albeit an inevitable one. Byron, who had a larger amount of common sense than any poet of his day, tells us, in "Bep-po,"

One hates an author that's all author; *fellows In foolscap uniforms turn'd up with ink.*

And his lordship's "hate" in the matter is under-standable enough. In his own day, Scott and himself were almost the only distinguished authors who were not "all authors," just as Mr. Helps and Sir Edward Bulwer Lytton are almost the only representatives of the class in ours. This professional taint not only resides in the writer, impairing his fulness and completion; it flows out of him into his work, and impairs it also. It is the professional character which authorship has assumed which has taken individuality and personal flavour from so much of our writing, and prevented to a large extent the production of enduring books. Our writing is done too hurriedly, and to serve a purpose too immediate. Literature is not so much an art as a manufacture. There is a demand, and too many crops are taken off the soil; it is never allowed to lie fallow, and to nourish itself in peacefulness and silence. When so many cups are to be filled, too much water is certain to be put into the teapot. Letters have become a profession, and probably of all professions it is, in the long run, the least conducive to personal happiness. It is the most precarious. In it, above all others, to be weak is to be miserable. It is the least mechanical, consequently the most exhausting; and in its higher walks it deals with a man's most vital material—utilises his emotions, trades on his faculties of love and imagination, uses for its own purposes the human heart by which he lives. These things a man requires for himself; and when they are in a large proportion transported to an ideal world, they make the ideal world all the more brilliant and furnished, and leave his ordinary existence all the more arid, and commonplace. You cannot spend money and have it;

you cannot use emotion and possess it. The poet who sings loudly of love and love's delights, may in the ordinary intercourse of life be all the colder for his singing. The man who has been moved while describing an imaginary death-bed to-day, is all the more likely to be unmoved while standing by his friend's grave to-morrow. Shakspeare, after emerging from the moonlight in the Verona orchard, and Romeo and Juliet's silvery interchange of vows, was, I fear me, not marvellously enamoured of the autumn on Ann Hathaway's cheek. It is in some such way as this that a man's books may impoverish his life; that the fire and heat of his genius may make his hearth all the colder. From considerations like these, one can explain satisfactorily enough to one's self the domestic misadventures of men of letters —of poets especially. We know the poets only in their books; their wives know them out of them. Their wives see the other side of the moon; and we have been made pretty well aware how they have appreciated *that*.

The man engaged in the writing of books is tempted to make such writing the be-all and end-all of his existence—to grow his literature out of his history, experience, or observation, as the gardener grows out of soils brought from a distance the plants which he intends to exhibit. The cup of life foams fiercely over into first books; materials for the second, third, and fourth must be carefully sought for. The man of letters, as time passes on and the professional impulse works deeper, ceases to regard the world with a single eye. The man slowly merges into the artist. He values new emotions and experiences, because he can turn these into artistic shapes. He plucks "copy" from rising and setting suns. He sees marketable pathos in his friend's death-bed. He carries the peal of his daughter's marriage-bells into his sentences or his rhymes; and in these the music sounds sweeter to him than in the sunshine and the wind. If originally of a meditative, introspective mood, his profession can hardly fail to confirm and deepen his peculiar temperament. He begins to feel his own pulse curiously, and for a purpose. As a spy in the service of literature, he lives in the world and its concerns. Out of everything he seeks thoughts and images, as out of everything the bee seeks wax and honey. A curious instance of this mode of looking at things occurs in Goethe's "Letters from Italy," with whom, indeed, it was a fashion, and who helped himself out of the teeming world to more effect than any man of his time:

"From Botzen to Trent the stage is nine leagues, and runs through a valley which constantly increases in fertility. All that merely struggles into vegetation on the higher mountains has here more strength and vitality. The sun shines with warmth, and there is once more belief in a Deity.

"A poor woman cried out to me to take her child into my vehicle, as the soil was burning its feet.

I did her this service out of honour to the strong light of Heaven. The child was strangely decked out, *but I could get nothing from it in any way.*"

It is clear that out of all this the reader gains; but I cannot help thinking that for the writer it tends to destroy entire and simple living—all hearty and final enjoyment in life. Joy and sorrow, death and marriage, the comic circumstance and the tragic, what befalls him, what he observes, what he is brought into contact with, do not affect him as they affect other men; they are secrets to be rifled, stones to be built with, clays to be moulded into artistic shape. In giving emotional material artistic form, there is indisputably a certain noble pleasure; but it is of a solitary and severe complexion, and takes a man out of the circle and sympathies of his fellows. I do not say that this kind of life makes a man selfish, but it often makes him *seem* so; and the results of this seeming, on friendship and the domestic relationships, for instance, are as baleful as if selfishness really existed. The peculiar temptation which besets men of letters, the curious playing with thought and emotion, the tendency to analyse and take everything to pieces, has two results, and neither aids his happiness nor even his literary success. On the one hand, and in relation to the social relations, it gives him somewhat of an icy aspect, and so breaks the spring and eagerness of affectionate response. For the best affection is shy, reticent, undemonstrative, and

[165]

needs to be drawn out by its like. If unrecognised like an acquaintance on the street, it passes by, making no sign, and is for the time being a stranger. On the other hand, the desire to say a fine thing about a phenomenon, whether natural or moral, prevents a man from reaching the inmost core of the phenomenon. Entrance into these matters will never be obtained by the most sedulous seeking. The man who has found an entrance cannot tell how he came there, and he will never find his way back again by the same road. From this law arise all the dreary conceits and artifices of the poets; it is through the operation of the same law that many of our simple songs and ballads are inexpressibly affecting, because in them there is no consciousness of authorship; emotion and utterance are twin-born, consentaneous—like sorrow and tears, a blow and its pain, a kiss and its thrill. When a man is happy, every effort to express his happiness mars its completeness. I am not happy at all unless I am happier than I know. When the tide is full there is silence in channel and creek. The silence of the lover when he clasps the maid is better than the passionate murmur of the song which celebrates her charms. If to be near the rose makes the nightingale tipsy with delight, what must it be to be the rose herself? One feeling of the "wild joys of living—the leaping from rock to rock," is better than the "muscular-Christianity" literature which our time has produced. I am afraid that the profession of

letters interferes with the elemental feelings of
life; and I am afraid, too, that in the majority
of cases this interference is not justified by its
results. The entireness and simplicity of life is
flawed by the intrusion of an inquisitive element,
and this inquisitive element never yet found
anything which was much worth the finding. Men
live by the primal energies of love, faith, imagination; and happily it is not given to every one to
live, in the pecuniary sense, by the artistic utilisa-
tion and sale of these. You cannot make ideas;
they must come unsought if they come at all.

From pastoral graves extracting thoughts divine

is a profitable occupation enough, if you stumble
on the little churchyard covered over with silence,
and folded among the hills. If you go to the
churchyard with intent to procure thoughts, as
you go into the woods to gather anemones, you
are wasting your time. Thoughts must come
naturally, like wild flowers; they cannot be forced
in a hotbed—even although aided by the leaf-
mould of your past—like exotics. And it is the
misfortune of men of letters of our day that they
cannot afford to wait for this natural flowering
of thought, but are driven to the forcing process,
with the results which were to be expected.

ON THE IMPORTANCE OF A
MAN TO HIMSELF

THE present writer remembers to have been visited once by a strange feeling of puzzlement; and the puzzled feeling arose out of the following circumstance: He was seated in a railway-carriage, five minutes or so before starting, and had time to contemplate certain waggons or trucks filled with cattle, drawn up on a parallel line, and quite close to the window at which he sat. The cattle wore a much-enduring aspect; and, as he looked into their large, patient, melancholy eyes—for, as before mentioned, there was no space to speak of intervening—the feeling of puzzlement alluded to arose in his mind. And it consisted in an attempt to solve the existence before him, to enter into it, to understand it, and his inability to accomplish it, or indeed to make any way toward the accomplishment of it. The much-enduring animals in the trucks opposite had unquestionably some rude twilight of a notion of a world; of objects they had some unknown cognizance; but he could not get behind the melancholy eye within a yard of him, and look through it. How, from that window, the world shaped itself, he could not discover, could not even fancy; and yet, staring on the animals, he was conscious of a certain fascination in which there lurked an element of terror. These wild, unkempt brutes, with slavering muzzles, penned together, lived, could choose between this thing and the other, could be frightened, could be enraged, could even love and hate; and gazing into a placid, heavy countenance, and the depths of a patient eye, not a yard away, he was conscious of an obscure and shuddering recognition, of a life akin so far with his own. But to enter into that life imaginatively, and to conceive it, he found impossible. Eye looked upon eye, but the one could not flash recognition on the other; and, thinking of this, he remembers with what a sense of ludicrous horror the idea came—what, if looking on one another thus, some spark of recognition could be elicited; if some rudiment of thought could be detected; if there were indeed a point at which man and ox could meet and compare notes? Suppose some gleam or scintillation of humour had lighted up the unwinking, amber eye? Heavens! the bellow of the weaning calf would be pathetic, shoe-leather would be forsworn, the eating of roast meat, hot or cold, would be cannibalism, the terrified world would make a sudden dash into vegetarianism! Happily, before fancy had time to play another vagary, with a snort and a pull the train moved on, and my truck-

ful of horned friends were left gazing into empty
space, with the same wistful, patient, and melancholy expression with which, for the space of five
minutes or so, they had surveyed and bewildered
me.

A similar feeling of puzzlement to that which
I have indicated besets one not unfrequently in
the contemplation of men and women. You are
brought in contact with a person, you attempt to
comprehend him, to enter into him, in a word
to *be* him, and, if you are not utterly foiled in the
attempt, you cannot flatter yourself that you have
been successful to the measure of your desire.
A person interests, or piques, or tantalises you,
you do your best to make him out, yet strive as
you will, you cannot read the riddle of his personality. From the invulnerable fortress of his
own nature he smiles contemptuously on the be-
leaguering armies of your curiosity and analysis.
And it is not only the stranger that thus defeats
you; it may be the brother brought up by the
same fireside with you, the best friend whom you
have known from early school and college days,
the very child, perhaps, that bears your name,
and with whose moral and mental apparatus you
think you are as familiar as with your own. In
the midst of the most amicable relationships and
the best understandings, human beings are, at
times, conscious of a cold feeling of strangeness—
the friend is actuated by a feeling which never
could actuate you, some hitherto unknown part

of his character becomes visible, and while at one moment you stood in such close neighbourhood that you could feel his arm touch your own, in the next there is a feeling of removal, of distance, of empty space betwixt him and you in which the wind is blowing. You and he become separate entities. He is related to you as Border peel is related to Border peel on Tweedside, or as ship is related to ship on the sea. It is not meant that any quarrel or direct misunderstanding should have taken place, simply that feeling of foreignness is meant to be indicated which occurs now and then in the intercourse of the most affectionate; which comes as a harsh reminder to friends and lovers that with whatsoever flowery bands they may be linked, they are separated persons, who understand, and *can* only understand, each other partially. It is annoying to be put out in our notions of men and women thus, and to be forced to rearrange them. It is a misfortune to have to manœuvre one's heart as a general has to manœuvre his army. The globe has been circumnavigated, but no man ever yet has; you may survey a kingdom and note the result in maps, but all the *savants* in the world could not produce a reliable map of the poorest human personality. And the worst of all this is, that love and friendship may be the outcome of a certain condition of knowledge; increase the knowledge, and love and friendship beat their wings and go. Every man's road in life is marked by the graves of his personal likings. Intimacy is frequently the road to indifference, and marriage, a parricide. From these accidents to the affections, and from the efforts to repair them, life has in many a patched and tinkered look.

Love and friendship are the discoveries of ourselves in others, and our delight in the recognition; and in men, as in books, we only know that, the parallel of which we have in ourselves. We know only that portion of the world which we have travelled over; and we are never a whit wiser than our own experiences. Imagination, the falcon, sits on the wrist of Experience, the falconer; she can never soar beyond the reach of his whistle, and when tired she must return to her perch. Our knowledge is limited by ourselves, and so also are our imaginations. And so it comes about, that a man measures everything by his own footrule; that if he is ignoble, all the ignobleness that is in the world looks out upon him, and claims kindred with him; if noble, all the nobleness in the world does the like. Shakspeare is always the same height with his reader; and when a thousand Christians subscribe to one Confession of Faith, hardly to two of them does it mean the same thing. The world is a great warehouse of raiment, to which every one has access and is allowed free use; and the remarkable thing is, what coarse stuffs are often chosen, and how scantily some people are attired.

We never get quit of ourselves. While I am

writing, the spring is outside, and this season of the year touches my spirit always with a sense of newness, of strangeness, of resurrection. It shoots boyhood again into the blood of middle age. That tender greening of the black bough and the red field—that coming again of the new-old flowers—that re-birth of love in all the family of birds, with cooings, and caressings, and building of nests in wood and brake—that strange glory of sunshine in the air—that stirring of life in the green mould, making even churchyards beautiful—seems like the creation of a new world. And yet—and yet, even with the lamb in the sunny field, the lark mile-high in the blue, Spring has her melancholy side, and bears a sadder burden to the heart than Autumn, preaching of decay with all his painted woods. For the flowers that make sweet the moist places in the forest are not the same that bloomed the year before. Another lark sings above the furrowed field. Nature rolls on in her eternal course, repeating her tale of spring, summer, autumn, winter; but life in man and beast is transitory, and other living creatures take their places. It is quite certain that one or other of the next twenty springs will come unseen by me, will awake no throb of transport in my veins. But will it be less bright on that account? Will the lamb be saddened in the field? Will the lark be less happy in the air? The sunshine will draw the daisy from the mound under which I sleep, as carelessly as she draws the cowslip from the meadow by the river-side. The seasons have no ruth, no compunction. They care not for our petty lives. The light falls sweetly on graveyards, and on brown labourers among the hay-swathes. Were the world depopulated to-morrow, next spring would break pitilessly bright, flowers would bloom, fruit-tree boughs wear pink and white; and although there would be no eye to witness, Summer would not adorn herself with one blossom the less. It is curious to think how important a creature a man is to himself. We cannot help thinking that all things exist for our particular selves. The sun, in whose light a system lives, warms *me*; makes the trees grow for me; paints the evening sky in gorgeous colours for me. The mould I till, produced from the beds of extinct oceans and the grating of rock and mountain during countless centuries, exists that I may have muffins to breakfast. Animal life, with its strange instincts and affections, is to be recognised and cherished—for does it not draw my burdens for me, and carry me from place to place, and yield me comfortable broadcloth, and succulent joints to dinner? I think it matter of complaint that Nature, like a personal friend to whom I have done kind services, will not wear crape at my funeral. I think it cruel that the sun should shine, and birds sing, and I lying in my grave. People talk of the age of the world! So far as I am concerned, it began with my consciousness, and will end with my decease.

IMPORTANCE OF A MAN TO HIMSELF

And yet, this self-consciousness, which so continually besets us, is in itself a misery and a galling chain. We are never happy till by imagination we are taken out of the pales and limits of self. We receive happiness at second hand: the spring of it may be in ourselves, but we do not know it to be happiness till, like the sun's light from the moon, it is reflected on us from an object outside. The admixture of a foreign element sweetens and unfamiliarises it. Sheridan prepared his good things in solitude, but he tasted for the first time his jest's prosperity when it came back to him in illumined faces and a roar of applause. Your oldest story becomes new when you have a new auditor. A young man is truth-loving and amiable; but it is only when these fair qualities shine upon him from a girl's face that he is smitten by transport—only then is he truly happy. In that junction of hearts, in that ecstasy of mutual admiration and delight, the finest epithalamium ever writ by poet is hardly worthy of the occasion. The countryman purchases oranges at a fair for his little ones; and when he brings them home in the evening, and watches his chubby urchins, sitting up among the bedclothes, peel and devour the fruit, he is for the time being richer than if he drew the rental of the orange-groves of Seville. To eat an orange himself is nothing; to see *them* eat it is a pleasure worth the price of the fruit a thousand times over. There is no happiness in the world in which love does not enter; and love is but the discovery of ourselves in others, and the delight in the recognition. Apart from others, no man can make his happiness; just as, apart from a mirror of one kind or another, no man can become acquainted with his own lineaments.

The accomplishment of a man is the light by which we are enabled to discover the limits of his personality. Every man brings into the world with him a certain amount of pith and force, and to that pith or force his amount of accomplishment is exactly proportioned. It is in this way that every spoken word, every action of a man, becomes biographical. Everything a man says or does is in consistency with himself; and it is by looking back on his sayings and doings that we arrive at the truth concerning him. A man is one; and every outcome of him has a family resemblance. Goldsmith did *not* "write like an angel and talk like poor Poll," as we may in part discern from Boswell's "Johnson." Strange, indeed, if a man talked continually the sheerest nonsense, and wrote continually the gracefulest humours; if a man was lame on the street, and the finest dancer in the ballroom. To describe a character by antithesis is like painting a portrait in black and white—all the curious intermixtures and gradations of colour are lost. The accomplishment of a human being is measured by his strength, or by his nice tact in using his strength. The distance to which your gun, whether rifled or smooth-bored, will carry its shot, depends upon the force of its charge. A runner's speed and endurance depends upon his depth of chest and elasticity of limb. If a poet's lines lack harmony, it instructs us that there is a certain lack of harmony in himself. We see why Haydon failed as an artist when we read his life. No one can dip into the "Excursion" without discovering that Wordsworth was devoid of humour, and that he cared more for the narrow Cumberland vale than he did for the big world. The flavour of opium can be detected in the "Ancient Mariner" and "Christabel." A man's word or deed takes us back to himself, as the sunbeam takes us back to the sun. It is the sternest philosophy, but on the whole the truest, that, in the wide arena of the world, failure and success are not accidents, as we so frequently suppose, but the strictest justice. If you do your fair day's work, you are certain to get your fair day's wage—in praise or pudding, whichever happens to suit your taste. You may have seen at country fairs a machine by which the rustics test vigorously their strength of arm. A country fellow strikes vigorously a buffer, which recoils, and the amount of the recoil—dependent, of course, on the force with which it is struck—is represented by a series of notches or marks. The world is such a buffer. A man strikes it with all his might: his mark may be £40,000, a peerage and Westminster Abbey, a name in literature or art; but in every case his mark is nicely determined by the force or the art with which the buffer is struck. Into

the world a man brings his personality, and his
biography is simply a catalogue of its results.

There are some men who have no individuality,
just as there are some men who have no face.
These are to be described by generals, not by
particulars. They are thin, vapid, inconclusive.
They are important solely on account of their
numbers. For them the census enumerator labours;
they form majorities; they crowd voting-booths;
they make the money; they do the ordinary work
of the world. They are valuable when well of-
ficered. They are plastic matter to be shaped by
a workman's hand; and are built with as bricks
are built with. In the aggregate, they form public
opinion; but then, in every age, public opinion is
the disseminated thoughts of some half a dozen
men, who are in all probability sleeping quietly
in their graves. They retain dead men's ideas,
just as the atmosphere retains the light and heat
of the set sun. They are not light—they are twilight. To know how to deal with such men—to
know how to use them—is the problem which ambitious force is called upon to solve. Personality,
individuality, force of character, or by whatever
name we choose to designate original and vigorous
manhood, is the best thing which nature has in
her gift. The forceful man is a prophecy of the
future. The wind blows here, but long after it is
spent, the big wave which is its creature breaks
on a shore a thousand miles away. It is curious
how swiftly influences travel from centre to cir-

cumference. A certain empress invents a gracefully pendulous crinoline, and immediately, from Paris to the Pole, the female world is behooped; and neither objurgation of brother, lover, or husband, deaths by burning or machinery, nor all the wit of the satirists, are likely to affect its vitality. Never did an idea go round civilisation so rapidly. Crinoline has already a heavier martyrology than many a creed. The world is used easily, if one can only hit on the proper method; and force of character, originality, of whatever kind, is always certain to make its mark. It is a diamond, and the world is its pane of glass. In a world so commonplace as this, the peculiar man even should be considered a blessing. Humorousness, eccentricity, the habit of looking at men and things from an odd angle, are valuable, because they break the dead level of society, and take away its sameness. It is well that a man should be known by something else than his name: there are few of us who can be known by anything else, and Brown, Jones, and Robinson are the names of the majority.

In literature and art this personal outcome is of the highest value; in fact, it is the only thing truly valuable. The greatness of an artist or a writer does not depend on what he has in common with other artists and writers, but on what he has peculiar to himself. The great man is the man who does a thing for the first time. It was a difficult thing to discover America; since it has been discovered, it has been found an easy enough task to sail thither. It is this peculiar something resident in a poem or a painting which is its final test—at all events, possessing it, it has the elements of endurance. Apart from its other values, it has, in virtue of that, a biographical one; it becomes a study of character; it is a window through which you can look into a human interior. There is a cleverness in the world which seems to have neither father nor mother. It exists, but it is impossible to tell from whence it comes—just as it is impossible to lift the shed apple-blossom of an orchard, and to discover, from its bloom and odour, to what branch it belonged. Such cleverness illustrates nothing: it is an anonymous letter. Look at it ever so long, and you cannot tell its lineage. It lives in the catalogue of waifs and strays. On the other hand, there are men whose every expression is characteristic, whose every idea seems to come out of a mould. In the short sentence, or curt, careless saying of such, when laid bare, you can read their histories so far, as in the smallest segment of a tree you can trace the markings of its rings. The first dies, because it is shallow-rooted, and has no vitality beyond its own; the second lives, because it is related to and fed by something higher than itself. The famous axiom of Mrs. Glass, that in order to make hare-soup you "must first catch your hare," has a wide significance. In art, literature, social life, morals even, you must first catch your man: that done, everything else follows as a matter of course. A man may learn much; but for the most important thing of all he can find neither teachers nor schools.

Each man is the most important thing in the world to himself; but why is he to himself so important? Simply because he is a personality with capacities of pleasure, of pain, who can be hurt, who can be pleased, who can be disappointed, who labours and expects his hire, in whose consciousness, in fact, for the time being, the whole universe lives. He is, and everything else is relative. Confined to his own personality, making it his tower of outlook, from which only he can survey the outer world, he naturally enough forms a rather high estimate of its value, of its dignity, of its intrinsic worth. This high estimate is useful in so far as it makes his condition pleasant, and it—or rather our proneness to form it— we are accustomed to call vanity. Vanity—which really helps to keep the race alive—has been treated harshly by the moralists and satirists. It does not quite deserve the hard names it has been called. It interpenetrates everything a man says or does, but it interpenetrates for a useful purpose. If it is always an alloy in the pure gold of virtue, it at least does the service of an alloy —making the precious metal workable. Nature gave man his powers, appetites, aspirations, and along with these a pan of incense, which fumes from the birth of consciousness to its decease, making the best part of life rapture, and the worst part endurable. But for vanity the race would have died out long ago. There are some men whose lives seem to us as undesirable as the lives of toads or serpents; yet these men breathe in tolerable content and satisfaction. If a man could hear all that his fellows say of him—that he is stupid, that he is henpecked, that he will be in the *Gazette* in a week, that his brain is softening, that he has said all his best things—and if he could believe that these pleasant things are true, he would be in his grave before the month was out. Happily no man does hear these things; and if he did, they would only provoke inextinguishable wrath or inextinguishable laughter. A man receives the shocks of life on the buffer of his vanity. Vanity acts as his second and bottle-holder in the world's prize-ring, and it fights him well, bringing him smilingly up to time after the fiercest knock-down blows. Vanity is to a man what the oily secretion is to a bird, with which it sleeks and adjusts the plumage ruffled by whatever causes. Vanity is not only instrumental in keeping a man alive and in heart, but, in its lighter manifestations, it is the great sweetener of social existence. It is the creator of dress and fashion; it is the inventor of forms and ceremonies; to it we are indebted for all our traditions of civility. For vanity in its idler moments is benevolent, is as willing to give pleasure as to take it, and accepts as sufficient reward for its services a kind word or an approving smile. It delights to bask in the sunshine of approbation. Out of man vanity makes *gentle*man. The proud man is cold, the selfish man hard and griping—the vain man desires to shine, to please, to make himself agreeable; and this amiable feeling works to the outside in suavity and charm of manner. The French are the vainest people in Europe, and the most polite.

As each man is to himself the most important thing in the world, each man is an egotist in his thinkings, in his desires, in his fears. It does not, however, follow that each man must be an egotist —as the word is popularly understood—in his speech. But even although this were the case, the world would be divided into egotists, likable and unlikable. There are two kinds of egotism, a trifling vainglorious kind, a mere burning of personal incense, in which the man is at once altar, priest, censer, and divinity; a kind which deals with the accidents and wrappages of the speaker, his equipage, his riches, his family, his servants, his furniture and array. The other kind has no taint of self-aggrandizement, but is rooted in the faculties of love and humour; and this latter kind is never offensive, because it includes others, and knows no scorn or exclusiveness. The one is the offspring of a narrow and unimaginative personality; the other of a large and genial one. There are persons who are the terrors of society. Perfectly innocent of evil intention, they are yet, with a certain brutal unconsciousness, continually trampling on other people's corns. They touch you every now and again like a red-hot iron. You wince, acquit them of any desire to wound, but find forgiveness a hard task. These persons remember everything about themselves, and forget everything about you. They have the instinct of a flesh-fly for a raw. Should your great-grandfather have had the misfortune to be hanged, such a person is certain, on some public occasion, to make allusion to your pedigree. He will probably insist on your furnishing him with a sketch of your family-tree. If your daughter has made a runaway marriage—on which subject yourself and friends maintain a judicious silence—he is certain to stumble upon it, and make the old sore smart again. In all this there is no malice, no desire to wound; it arises simply from want of imagination, from profound immersion in self. An imaginative man recognises at once a portion of himself in his fellow, and speaks to that. To hurt you is to hurt himself. Much of the rudeness we encounter in life cannot be properly set down to cruelty or badness of heart. The unimaginative man is callous, and although he hurts easily, he cannot be easily hurt in return. The imaginative man is sensitive and merciful to others out of the merest mercy to himself.

In literature, as in social life, the attractiveness of egotism depends entirely upon the egotist. If he be a conceited man, full of self-admirations and vainglories, his egotism will disgust and repel. When he sings his own praises, his reader feels that reflections are being thrown on himself, and in a natural revenge he calls the writer a coxcomb. If, on the other hand, he be loving, genial, humorous, with a sympathy for others, his garrulousness and his personal allusions are forgiven, because while revealing himself, he is revealing his reader as well. A man may write about himself during his whole life without once tiring or offending; but to accomplish this, he must be interesting in himself—be a man of curious and vagrant moods, gifted with the cunningest tact and humour; and the experience which he relates must at a thousand points touch the experiences of his readers so that they, as it were, become partners in his game. When X tells me, with an evident swell of pride, that he dines constantly with half a dozen menservants in attendance, or that he never drives abroad save in a coach-and-six, I am not conscious of any special gratitude to X for the information. Possibly, if my establishment boasts only of Cinderella, and if a cab is the only vehicle in which I can afford to ride, and all the more if I can indulge in *that* only on occasions of solemnity, I fly into a rage, pitch the book to the other end of the room, and may never afterwards be brought to admit that X is possessor of a solitary ounce of brains. If, on the other hand, Z informs me that every February he goes out to the leafless woods to hunt early snowdrops, and brings home bunches of them in his hat; or that he prefers in woman a brown eye to a blue, and explains by early love passages his reasons for the preference, I do not get angry; on the contrary, I feel quite pleased; perhaps, if the matter is related with unusual grace and tenderness, it is read with a certain moisture and dimness of eye. And the reason is obvious. The egotistical X is barren, and suggests nothing beyond himself, save that he is a good deal better off than I am—a reflection much pleasanter to him than it is to me; whereas the equally egotistical Z, with a single sentence about his snowdrops, or his liking for brown eyes rather than for blue, sends my thoughts wandering away back among my dead spring-times, or wafts me the odours of the roses of those summers when the colour of an eye was of more importance than it now is. X's men-servants and coach-and-six do not fit into the life of his reader, because in all probability his reader knows as much about these things as he knows about Pharaoh; Z's snowdrops and preferences of colour do, because every one knows what the spring thirst is, and every one in his time has been enslaved by eyes whose colour he could not tell for his life, but which he knew were the tenderest that ever looked love, the brightest that ever flashed sunlight. Montaigne and Charles Lamb are egotists of the Z class, and the world never wearies reading them; nor are egotists of the X school absolutely without entertainment. Several of these the world reads assiduously too, although for another reason. The avid vanity of Mr. Pepys would be gratified if made aware of the success of his Diary; but curiously to inquire into the reason of that success, *why* his Diary has been found so amusing, would not conduce to his comfort.

After all, the only thing a man knows is himself. The World outside he can know only by hearsay. His shred of personality is all he has; than that, he is nothing richer, nothing poorer. Everything else is mere accident and appendage. Alexander must not be measured by the shoutings of his armies, nor Lazarus at Dives' gates by his sores. And a man knows himself only in part. In every nature, as in Australia, there is an unexplored territory—green, well-watered regions or mere sandy deserts; and into that territory experience is making progress day by day. We can remember when we knew only the outer childish rim—and from the crescent guessed the sphere; whether, as we advanced, these guesses have been realised, each knows for himself.

A SHELF IN MY BOOKCASE

WHEN a man glances critically through the circle of his intimate friends, he is obliged to confess that they are far from being perfect. They possess neither the beauty of Apollo, nor the wisdom of Solon, nor the wit of Mercutio, nor the reticence of Napoleon III. If pushed hard he will be constrained to admit that he has known each and all get angry without sufficient occasion, make at times the foolishest remarks, and act as if personal comfort were the highest thing in their estimation. Yet, driven thus to the wall, forced to make such uncomfortable confessions, our supposed man does not like his friends one whit the less; nay, more, he is aware that if they were very superior and faultless persons he would not be conscious of so much kindly feeling towards them. The tide of friendship does not rise high on the bank of perfection. Amiable weaknesses and shortcomings are the food of love. It is from the roughnesses and imperfect breaks in a man that you are able to lay hold of him. If a man be an entire and perfect chrysolite, you slide off him and fall back into ignorance. My friends are not perfect—no more am I—and so we suit each other admirably. Their weaknesses keep mine in countenance, and so save me from humiliation and shame. We give and take, bear and forbear; the stupidity they utter to-day salves the recollection of the stupidity I uttered yesterday; in their want of wit I see my own, and so feel satisfied and kindly disposed. It is one of the charitable dispensations of Providence that perfection is not essential to friendship. If I had to seek my perfect man, I should wander the world a good while, and when I found him, and was down on my knees before him, he would, to a certainty, turn the cold shoulder on me—and so life would be an eternal search, broken by the coldness of repulse and loneliness. Only to the perfect being in an imperfect world, or the imperfect being in a perfect world, is everything irretrievably out of joint.

On a certain shelf in the bookcase which stands in the room in which I am at present sitting—bookcase surmounted by a white Dante, looking out with blind, majestic eyes—are collected a number of volumes which look somewhat the worse for wear. Those of them which originally possessed gilding have had it fingered off, each of them has leaves turned down, and they open of themselves at places wherein I have been happy, and with whose every word I am familiar as with the furniture of the room in which I nightly slum-

ber; each of them has remarks relevant and irrelevant scribbled on their margins. These favourite volumes cannot be called peculiar glories of
literature; but out of the world of books have I
singled them, as I have singled my intimates out
of the world of men. I am on easy terms with them,
and feel that they are no higher than my heart.
Milton is not there, neither is Wordsworth; Shakspeare, if he had written comedies only, would
have been there to a certainty, but the presence
of the *five* great tragedies—Hamlet, Othello, Macbeth, Lear, Antony and Cleopatra—for this last
should be always included among his supreme
efforts—has made me place him on the shelf where
the mighty men repose, himself the mightiest of
all. Reading Milton is like dining off gold plate
in a company of kings; very splendid, very cere-
monious, and not a little appalling. Him I read
but seldom, and only on high days and festivals
of the spirit. Him I never lay down without feeling
my appreciation increased for lesser men—never
without the same kind of comfort that one returning from the presence feels when he doffs respectful attitude and dress of ceremony, and subsides
into old coat, familiar arm-chair, and slippers.
After long-continued organ-music, the jangle of
the Jew's harp is felt as an exquisite relief. With
the volumes on the special shelf I have spoken of,
I am quite at home, and I feel somehow as if
they were at home with me. And as to-day the
trees bend to the blast, and the rain comes in

dashes against my window, and as I have nothing to do and cannot get out, and wish to kill the hours in as pleasant a manner as I can, I shall even talk about them, as in sheer liking a man talks about the trees in his garden, or the pictures on his wall. I can't expect to say anything very new or striking, but I can give utterance to sincere affection, and that is always pleasant to one's self and generally not ungrateful to others.

First, then, on this special shelf stands Nathaniel Hawthorne's "Twice-Told Tales." It is difficult to explain why I like these short sketches and essays, written in the author's early youth, better than his later, more finished, and better-known novels and romances. The world sets greater store by "The Scarlet Letter" and "Transformation" than by this little book—and, in such matters of liking, against the judgment of the world there is no appeal. I think the reason of my liking consists in this—that the novels were written for the world, while the tales seem written for the author; in these he is actor and audience in one. Consequently, one gets nearer him, just as one gets nearer an artist in his first sketch than in his finished picture. And after all, one takes the greatest pleasure in those books in which a peculiar personality is most clearly revealed. A thought may be very commendable *as* a thought, but I value it chiefly as a window through which I can obtain insight on the thinker; and Mr. Haw-

thorne's personality is peculiar, and specially peculiar in a new country like America. He is quiet,
fanciful, quaint, and his humour is shaded by
a certain meditativeness of spirit. Although a
Yankee, he partakes of none of the characteristics
of a Yankee. His thinking and his style have an
antique air. His roots strike down through the
visible mould of the present, and draw sustenance
from the generations under ground. The ghosts
that haunt the chamber of his mind are the ghosts
of dead men and women. He has a strong smack
of the Puritan; he wears around him, in the New
England town, something of the darkness and
mystery of the aboriginal forest. He is a shy,
silent, sensitive, much-ruminating man, with no
special overflow of animal spirits. He loves solitude
and the things which age has made reverent. There
is nothing modern about him. Emerson's writing
has a cold cheerless glitter, like the new furniture
in a warehouse, which will come of use by and by;
Hawthorne's, the rich, subdued colour of furniture
in a Tudor mansion-house—which has winked
to long-extinguished fires, which has been toned
by the usage of departed generations. In many of
the "Twice-Told Tales" this peculiar personality
is charmingly exhibited. He writes of the street
or of the sea-shore, his eye takes in every object,
however trifling, and on these he hangs comments
melancholy and humorous. He does not require
to go far for a subject; he will stare on the puddles
in the street of a New England village, and im-

mediately it becomes a Mediterranean Sea with empires lying on its muddy shores. If the sermon be written out fully in your heart, almost any text will be suitable—if you have to find your sermon *in* your text, you may search the Testament, New and Old, and be as poor at the close of Revelation as when you started at the first book of Genesis. Several of the papers which I like best are monologues, fanciful, humorous, or melancholy; and of these my chief favourites are—"Sunday at Home," "Night Sketches," "Footprints on the Sea-shore," and the "Seven Vagabonds." This last seems to me almost the most exquisite thing which has flowed from its author's pen—a perfect little drama, the place a showman's waggon, the time the falling of a summer shower, full of subtle suggestions, which, if followed, will lead the reader away out of the story altogether; and illuminated by a grave, wistful kind of humour, which plays in turns upon the author's companions, and upon the author himself. Of all Mr. Hawthorne's gifts, this gift of humour—which would light up the skull and cross-bones of a village churchyard, which would be silent at a dinner-table—is to me the most delightful.

Then this writer has a strangely weird power. He loves ruins like the ivy, he skims the twilight like the bat, he makes himself a familiar of the phantoms of the heart and brain. He believes in ghosts; perhaps he has seen one burst on him from the impalpable air. He is fascinated by the jarred

brain and the ruined heart. Other men collect
china, books, pictures, jewels; this writer collects
singular human experiences, ancient wrongs and
agonies, murders done on unfrequented roads,
crimes that seem to have no motive, and all
the dreary mysteries of the world of will. To his
chamber of horrors Madame Tussaud's is nothing.
With proud, prosperous, healthy men, Mr. Hawthorne has little sympathy; he prefers a cracked
piano to a new one, he likes cobwebs in the corners
of his rooms. All this peculiar taste comes out
strongly in the little book in whose praise I am
writing. I read "The Minister's Black Veil," and
find it the first sketch of "The Scarlet Letter."
In "Wakefield"—the story of the man who left
his wife, remaining away twenty years, but who
yet looked upon her every day to appease his
burning curiosity as to her manner of enduring his
absence—I find the keenest analysis of an almost
incomprehensible act. And then Mr. Hawthorne
has a skill in constructing allegories which no one
of his contemporaries, either English or American,
possesses. These allegorical papers may be read
with pleasure, for their ingenuity, their grace,
their poetical feeling; but just as, gazing on the
surface of a stream, admiring the ripples and ed-
dies and the widening rings made by the butterfly
falling into it, you begin to be conscious that there
is something at the bottom, and gradually a dead
face wavers upwards from the oozy weeds, becoming every moment more clearly defined, so

through Mr. Hawthorne's graceful sentences, if read attentively, begins to flash the hidden meaning, a meaning, perhaps, the writer did not care to express formally and in set terms, and which he merely suggests and leaves the reader to make out for himself. If you have the book I am writing about, turn up "David Swan," "The Great Carbuncle," "The Fancy Show-box," and after you have read these, you will understand what I mean.

The next two books on my shelf—books at this moment leaning on the "Twice-Told Tales"—are Professor Aytoun's "Ballads of Scotland," and the "Lyra Germanica." These books I keep side by side with a purpose. The forms of existence with which they deal seem widely separated; but a strong kinship exists between them for all that. I open Professor Aytoun's book, and all this modern life—with its railways, its newspapers, its crowded cities, its Lancashire distresses, its debates in Parliament—fades into nothingness and silence. Scotland, from Edinburgh rock to the Tweed, stretches away in rude spaces of moor and forest. The wind blows across it, unpolluted by the smoke of towns. That which lives now has not yet come into existence; what are to-day crumbling and ivied ruins, are warm with household fires, and filled with human activities. Every Border keep is a home: brides are taken there in their blushes; children are born there; gray men, the crucifix held over them, die there. The moon dances on a plump of spears, as the moss-troopers, by secret and desert paths, ride over into England to lift a prey, and the bale-fire on the hill gives the alarm to Cumberland. Men live and marry, and support wife and little ones by steel-jacket and spear; and the Flower of Yarrow, when her larder is empty, claps a pair of spurs in her husband's platter. A time of strife and foray, of plundering and burning, of stealing and reaving; when hate waits half a lifetime for revenge, and where difficulties are solved by the slash of a swordblade. I open the German book, and find a warfare conducted in a different manner. Here the Devil rides about wasting and destroying. Here temptations lie in wait for the soul; here pleasures, like glittering meteors, lure it into marshes and abysses. Watch and ward are kept here, and to sleep at the post is death. Fortresses are built on the rock of God's promises—inaccessible to the arrows of the wicked—and therein dwell many trembling souls. Conflict rages around, not conducted by Border spear on barren moorland, but by weapons of faith and prayer in the devout German heart; a strife earnest as the other, with issues of life and death. And the resemblance between the books lies in this, that when we open them these past experiences and conditions of life gleam visibly to us far down like submerged cities —all empty and hollow now, though once filled with life as real as our own—through transparent waters.

In glancing over these German hymns, one is struck by their adaptation to the seasons and occurrences of ordinary life. Obviously, too, the writers' religion was not a Sunday matter only: it had its place in week-days as well. In these hymns there is little gloom; a healthy human cheerfulness pervades many of them, and this is surely as it ought to be. These hymns, as I have said, are adapted to the occasions of ordinary life, and this speaks favourably of the piety which produced them. I do not suppose that we English are less religious than other nations, but we are undemonstrative in this, as in most things. We have the sincerest horror of over-dressing ourselves in fine sentiments. We are a little shy of religion. We give it a day entirely to itself, and make it a stranger to the other six. We confine it in churches, or in the closet at home, and never think of taking it with us to the street, or into our business, or with us to the festival, or the gathering of friends. Dr. Arnold used to complain that he could get religious subjects treated in a masterly way, but could not get common subjects treated in a religious spirit. The Germans have done better: they have melted down the Sunday into the week. They have hymns embodying confessions of sin, hymns in the near prospect of death; and they have—what is more important—spiritual songs that may be sung by soldiers on the march, by the artisan at the loom, by the peasant following his team, by the mother among her children, and

by the maiden sitting at her wheel listening for
the step of her lover. Religion is thus brought in
to refine and hallow the sweet necessities and emotions of life, to cheer its weariness, and to exalt
its sordidness. The German life revolves like the
village festival with the pastor in the midst—joy
and laughter and merry games do not fear the
holy man, for he wears no unkindness in his eye,
but his presence checks everything boisterous or
unseemly—the rude word, the petulant act—and
when it has run its course, he uplifts his hands and
leaves his benediction on his children.

The "Lyra Germanica" contains the utterances
of pious German souls in all conditions of life
during many centuries. In it hymns are to be
found written not only by poor clergymen, and
still poorer precentors, by riband manufacturers
and shoemakers, who, amid rude environments,
had a touch of celestial melody in their hearts,
but by noble ladies and gentlemen, and crowned
kings. The oldest in the collection is one written
by King Robert of France about the year 1000.
It is beautifully simple and pathetic. State is
laid aside with the crown, pride with the royal
robe, and Lazarus at Dives' gate could not have
written out of a lowlier heart. The kingly brow
may bear itself high enough before men, the voice
may be commanding and imperious enough, cutting through contradiction as with a sword, but
before the Highest all is humbleness and bended
knees. Other compositions there are, scattered

through the volume, by great personages—several by Louisa Henrietta, Electress of Brandenburg, and Anton Ulrick, Duke of Brunswick—all written two hundred years ago. These are genuine poems, full of faith and charity, and calm trust in God. They are all dead now, these noble gentlemen and gentlewomen; their warfare, successful or adverse, has been long closed; but they gleam yet in my fancy, like the white effigies on tombs in dim cathedrals, the marble palms pressed together on the marble breast, the sword by the side of the knight, the psalter by the side of the lady, and flowing around them the scrolls on which are inscribed the texts of resurrection.

This book contains surely one of the most touching of human compositions—a song of Luther's. The great Reformer's music resounds to this day in our churches; and one of the rude hymns he wrote has such a step of thunder in it, that the father of Frederick the Great, Mr. Carlyle tells us, used to call it "God Almighty's Grenadier March." This one I speak of is of another mood, and is soft as tears. To appreciate it thoroughly, one must think of the burly, resolute, humorous, and withal tender-hearted man, and of the work he accomplished. He it was, the Franklin's kite, led by the highest hand, that went up into the papal thunder-cloud hanging black over Europe; and the angry fire that broke upon it burned it not, and in roars of boltless thunder the apparition collapsed, and the sun of truth broke through the inky fragments on the nations once again. He it was who, when advised not to trust himself in Worms, declared, "Although there be as many devils in Worms as there are tiles on the house-tops, I will go." He it was who, when brought to bay in the splendid assemblage, said, "It is neither safe nor prudent to do aught against conscience. Here stand I—I cannot do otherwise. God help me. Amen." The rock cannot move—the lightnings may splinter it. Think of these things, and then read Luther's "Christmas Carol," with its tender inscription. "Luther—written for his little son Hans, 1546." Coming from another pen, the stanzas were perhaps not much; coming from *his*, they move one like the finest eloquence. This song sunk deep into the hearts of the common people, and is still sung from the dome of the Kreuz Kirche in Dresden before daybreak on Christmas morning.

There is no more delightful reading in the world than these Scottish ballads. The mailed knight, the Border peel, the moonlight raid, the lady at her bower window—all these have disappeared from the actual world, and lead existence now as songs. Verses and snatches of these ballads are continually haunting and twittering about my memory, as in summer the swallows haunt and twitter about the eaves of my dwelling. I know them so well, and they meet a mortal man's experience so fully, that I am sure—with, perhaps, a little help from Shakspeare—I could conduct the whole of my business by quotation,—do all its love-making, pay all its tavern-scores, quarrel and make friends again in their words, far better than I could in my own. If you know these ballads, you will find that they mirror perfectly your every mood. If you are weary and down-hearted, behold, a verse starts to your memory trembling with the very sigh you have heaved. If you are merry, a stanza is dancing to the tune of your own mirth. If you love, be you ever so much a Romeo, here is the finest language for your using. If you hate, here are words which are daggers. If you like battle, here for two hundred years have trumpets been blowing and banners flapping. If you are dying, plentiful are the broken words here which have hovered on failing lips. Turn where you will, some fragment of a ballad is sure to meet you. Go into the loneliest places of experience and passion, and you discover that you are walking in human footprints. If you should happen to lift the first volume of Professor Aytoun's "Ballads of Scotland," the book of its own accord will open at "Clerk Saunders," and by that token you will guess that the ballad has been read and re-read a thousand times. And what a ballad it is! The story in parts is somewhat perilous to deal with, but with what instinctive delicacy the whole matter is managed! Then what tragic pictures, what pathos, what manly and womanly love! Just fancy how the sleeping lovers, the raised torches, and the faces of the seven brothers looking on, would gleam on the canvas of Mr. Millais!—

> *"For in may come my seven bauld brothers,*
> *Wi' torches burning bright."*

> *It was about the midnight hour,*
> *And they were fa'en asleep,*
> *When in and came her seven brothers,*
> *And stood at her bed feet.*

> *Then out and spake the first o' them,*
> *"We'll awa' and let them be."*
> *Then out and spake the second o' them,*
> *"His father has nae mair than he."*

> *Then out and spake the third o' them,*
> *"I wot they are lovers dear."*
> *Then out and spake the fourth o' them,*
> *"They ha'e lo'ed for mony a year."*

> *Then out and spake the fifth o' them,*
> *"It were sin true love to twain."*
> *"'Twere shame," out spake the sixth o' them,*
> *"To slay a sleeping man!"*

> *Then up and gat the seventh o' them,*
> *And never a word spake he,*
> *But he has striped his bright-brown brand*
> *Through Saunders's fair bodie.*

Clerk Saunders he started, and Margaret she turn'd
  Into his arms as asleep she lay,
And sad and silent was the night
  That was atween thir twae.

Could a word be added or taken from these verses without spoiling the effect? You never think of the language, so vividly is the picture impressed on the imagination. I *see* at this moment the sleeping pair, the bright-burning torches, the lowering faces of the brethren, and the one fiercer and darker than the others.

Pass we now to the Second Part—

  Sae painfully she clam' the wa',
    She clam' the wa' up after him;
  Hosen nor shoon upon her feet
    She had na time to put them on.

  "Is there ony room at your head, Saunders?
    Is there ony room at your feet?
  Or ony room at your side, Saunders,
    Where fain, fain I wad sleep?"

In that last line the very heart-strings crack. She is to be pitied far more than Clerk Saunders, lying stark with the cruel wound beneath his side, the love-kisses hardly cold yet upon his lips.

It may be said that the books of which I have been speaking attain to the highest literary excellence by favour of simplicity and unconsciousness.

[203]

Neither the German nor the Scotsman considered himself an artist. The Scot sings a successful foray, in which perhaps he was engaged, and he sings as he fought. In combat he did not dream of putting himself in a heroic position, or of flourishing his blade in a manner to be admired. A thrust of a lance would soon have finished him if he had. The pious German is overladen with grief, or touched by some blessing into sudden thankfulness, and he breaks into song as he laughs from gladness or groans from pain. This directness and naturalness give Scotch ballad and German hymn their highest charm. The poetic gold, if rough and unpolished, and with no elaborate devices carved upon it, is free at least from the alloy of conceit and sim- ulation. Modern writers might, with benefit to themselves, barter something of their finish and dexterity for that pure innocence of nature, and child-like simplicity and fearlessness, full of its own emotion, and unthinking of others or of their opinions, which characterise these old writings.

The eighteenth century must ever remain the most brilliant and interesting period of English literary history. It is interesting not only on ac- count of its splendour, but because it is so well known. We are familiar with the faces of its great men by portraits, and with the events of their lives by innumerable biographies. Every reader is ac- quainted with Pope's restless jealousy, Goldsmith's pitted countenance and plum-coloured coat, John- son's surly manners and countless eccentricities, and with the tribe of poets who lived for months ignorant of clean linen, who were hunted by bailiffs, who smelt of stale punch, and who wrote descriptions of the feasts of the gods in twopenny cook-shops. Manners and modes of thought had greatly changed since the century before. Macbeth, in silk stockings and scarlet coat, slew King Duncan, and the pit admired the wild force occasionally exhibited by the barbarian Shakspeare. In those days the Muse wore patches, and sat in a sumptuous boudoir, and her worshippers surrounded her in high-heeled shoes, ruffles, and powdered wigs. When the poets wished to paint nature, they described Chloe sitting on a green bank watching her sheep, or sighing when Strephon confessed his flame. And yet, with all this apparent shallowness, the age was earnest enough in its way. It was a good hater. It was filled with relentless literary feuds. Just recall the lawless state of things on the Scottish Border in the olden time—the cattle-lifting, the house-burning, the midnight murders, the powerful marauders, who, safe in numerous retainers and moated keep, bade defiance to law—recall this state of things, and imagine the quarrels and raids literary, the weapons satire and wit, and you have a good idea of the darker aspect of the time. There were literary bravoes, who hired themselves to assassinate reputations. There were literary reavers, who laid desolate at a foray a whole generation of wits. There were literary duels, fought out in grim hate to the very death. It was dangerous to interfere in the literary *mêlée*. Every now and then a fine gentleman was run through with a jest, or a foolish Maecenas stabbed to the heart with an epigram, and his foolishness settled for ever.

As a matter of course, on this special shelf of books will be found Boswell's "Life of Johnson"— a work in our literature unique, priceless. That altogether unvenerable yet profoundly-venerating Scottish gentleman—that queerest mixture of qualities, of force and weakness, blindness and insight, vanity and solid worth—has written the finest book of its kind which our nation possesses. It is quite impossible to overstate its worth. You lift it, and immediately the intervening years disappear, and you are in the presence of the Doctor. You are made free of the last century, as you are free of the present. You double your existence. The book is a letter of introduction to a whole knot of departed English worthies. In virtue of Boswell's labours, we know Johnson—the central man of his time—better than Burke did, or Reynolds— far better even than Boswell did. We know how he expressed himself, in what grooves his thoughts ran, how he dressed, how he ate, drank, and slept. Boswell's unconscious art is wonderful, and so is the result attained. This book has arrested, as never book did before, time and decay. Bozzy is really a wizard: he makes the sun stand still. Till his work is done, the future stands respectfully aloof. Out of ever-shifting time he has made fixed and permanent certain years, and in these Johnson talks and argues, while Burke listens, and Reynolds takes snuff, and Goldsmith, with hollowed hand, whispers a sly remark to his neighbour. There have they sat, these ghosts, for seventy years now, looked at and listened to by the passing generations; and there they still sit, the one voice going on! Smile at Boswell as we may, he was a spiritual phenomenon quite as rare as Johnson. More than most he deserves our gratitude. Let us hope that when next Heaven sends England a man like Johnson, a companion and listener like Boswell will be provided. The Literary Club sits for ever. What if the Mermaid were in like eternal session, with Shakspeare's laughter ringing through the fire and hail of wit!

By the strangest freak of chance or liking, the next book on my shelf contains the poems of Ebenezer Elliott, the Corn-law Rhymer. This volume, adorned by a hideous portrait in lithograph of the author, I can well remember picking up at a bookstall for a few pence many years ago. It seems curious to me that this man is not in these days better known. A more singular man has seldom existed—seldom a more genuine. His first business speculation failed, but when about forty he commenced again, and this time fortune made amends for her former ill-treatment. His warehouse was a small, dingy place, filled with bars of iron, with a bust of Shakspeare looking down on the whole. His country-house contained busts of

Achilles, Ajax, and Napoleon. Here is a poet who earned a competence as an iron-merchant; here is a monomaniac on the Corn-laws, who loved nature as intensely as ever did Burns or Wordsworth. Here is a John Bright uttering himself in fiery and melodious verse—Apollo with iron-dust on his face, wandering among the Sheffield knife-grinders! If you wish to form some idea of the fierce discontent which thirty years ago existed amongst the working men of England, you should read the Corn-law Rhymes. The Corn-laws are to him the twelve plagues of Egypt rolled together. On account of them, he denounces his country as the Hebrew prophets were wont to denounce Tyre and Sidon. His rage breaks out into curses, which are *not* forgiveness. He is maddened by the memory of Peterloo. Never, perhaps, was a sane human being so tyrannised over by a single idea. A skeleton was found on one of the Derbyshire hills. Had the man been crossed in love? had he crept up there to die in presence of the stars? "Not at all," cries Elliott; "he was a victim of the Corn-laws, who preferred dying on the mountain-top to receiving parish pay." In his wild poem all the evil kings in Hades descend from their thrones when King George enters. They only let slip the dogs of war; *he* taxed the people's bread. "Sleep on, proud Britoness!" he exclaims over a woman at rest in the grave she had purchased. In one of his articles in *Tait's Magazine*, he seriously proposed that tragedies should be written shewing the evils of the Corn-laws, and that on a given night they should be performed in every theatre of the kingdom, so that the nation might, by the speediest possible process, be converted to the gospel of Free-trade. In his eyes the Corn-laws had gathered into their black bosoms every human wrong; repeal them, and lo! the new heavens and the new earth! A poor and shallow theory of the universe, you will say; but it is astonishing what poetry he contrives to extract out of it. It is hardly possible, without quotation, to give an idea of the rage and fury which pervade these poems. He curses his political opponents with his whole heart and soul. He pillories them, and pelts them with dead cats and rotten eggs. The earnestness of his mood has a certain terror in it for meek and quiet people. His poems are of the angriest, but their anger is not altogether undivine. His scorn blisters and scalds, his sarcasm flays; but then outside nature is constantly touching him with a summer breeze or a branch of pink and white apple-blossom, and his mood becomes tenderness itself. He is far from being lachrymose; and when he is pathetic, he affects one as when a strong man sobs. His anger is not nearly so frightful as his tears. I cannot understand why Elliott is so little read. Other names not particularly remarkable I meet in the current reviews—his never. His book stands on my shelf, but on no other have I seen it. This I think strange, because, apart from the intrinsic value of his verse *as* verse, it has an historical value. Evil times, and embittered feelings, now happily passed away, are preserved in his books, like Pompeii and Herculaneum in Vesuvian lava. He was a poet of the poor, but in a quite peculiar sense. Burns, Crabbe, Wordsworth, were poets of the poor, but mainly of the peasant poor. Elliott is the poet of the English artizans— men who read newspapers and books, who are members of mechanics' institutes, who attend debating societies, who discuss political measures and political men, who are tormented by ideas—a very different kind of persons altogether. It is easier to find poetry beneath the blowing hawthorn than beneath the plumes of factory or furnace smoke. In such uninviting atmospheres Ebenezer Elliott found his; and I am amazed that the world does not hold it in greater regard, if for nothing else than for its singularity.

There is many another book on my shelf on which I might dilate, but this gossiping must be drawn to a close. When I began, the wind was bending the trees, and the rain came against the window in quick, petulant dashes. For hours now, wind and rain have ceased, the trees are motionless, the garden walk is dry. The early light of wintry sunset is falling across my paper, and, as I look up, the white Dante opposite is dipped in tender rose. Less stern he looks, but not less sad, than he did in the morning. The sky is clear, and an arm of bleak pink vapour stretches up into its depths. The air is cold with frost, and the rain which those dark clouds in the east hold will fall during the night in silent, feathery flakes. When I wake to-morrow, the world will be changed, frosty forests will cover my bedroom panes, the tree branches will be furred with snows; and to the crumbs which it is my daily custom to sprinkle on the shrubbery walk will come the lineal descendant of the charitable redbreast that covered up with leaves the sleeping children in the wood.

GEOFFREY CHAUCER

CHAUCER is admitted on all hands to be a great poet, but, by the general public at least, he is not frequently read. He is like a cardinal virtue, a good deal talked about, a good deal praised, honoured by a vast amount of distant admiration, but with little practical acquaintance. And for this there are many and obvious reasons. He is an ancient, and the rich old mahogany is neglected for the new and glittering veneer. He is occasionally gross; often tedious and obscure; he frequently leaves a couple of lovers to cite the opinions of Greek and Roman authors; and practice and patience are required to melt the frost of his orthography, and let his music flow freely. In the conduct of his stories he is garrulous, homely, and slow-paced. He wrote in a leisurely world, when there was plenty of time for writing and reading; long before the advent of the printer's devil or of Mr. Mudie. There is little of the lyrical element in him. He does not dazzle by sentences. He is not quotable. He does not shine in extracts so much as in entire poems. There is a pleasant equality about his writing: he advances through a story at an even pace, glancing round him on everything with curious, humorous eyes, and having his say about everything. He is the prince of story-tellers, and however much he may move others, he is not moved himself. His mood is so kindly that he seems always to have written after dinner, or after hearing good news—that he had received from the king another grant of wine, for instance—and he discourses of love and lovers' raptures, and the disappointments of life, half sportively, half sadly, like one who has passed through all, felt the sweetness and the bitterness of it, and been able to strike a balance. He had his share of crosses and misfortunes, but his was a nature which time and sorrow could only mellow and sweeten; and for all that had come and gone, he loved his "books clothed in black and red," to sit at good men's feasts; and if silent at table, as the Countess of Pembroke reported, the "stain upon his lip was wine." Chaucer's face is to his writings the best preface and commentary; it is contented-looking, like one familiar with pleasant thoughts, shy and self-contained somewhat, as if he preferred his own company to the noisy and rude companionship of his fellows; and the outlines are bland, fleshy, voluptuous, as of one who had a keen relish for the pleasures that leave no bitter traces. Tears and mental trouble, and the agonies of doubt, you cannot think of in connexion with it; laughter is sheathed in it, the light of a smile is diffused over it. In face and turn of genius he differs in every respect from his successor, Spenser; and in truth, in Chaucer and Spenser we see the fountains of the two main streams of British song: the one flowing through the drama and the humorous narrative, the other through the epic and the didactic poem. Chaucer rooted himself firmly in fact, and looked out upon the world in a half humorous, half melancholy mood. Spenser had but little knowledge of men as *men;* the cardinal virtues were the personages he was acquainted with; in everything he was "high fantastical," and, as a consequence, he exhibits neither humour nor pathos. Chaucer was thoroughly national; his characters, place them where he may—in Thebes or Tartary—are natives of one or other of the English shires. Spenser's genius was country-less as Ariel; search ever so diligently, you will not find an English daisy in all his enchanted forests. Chaucer was tolerant of everything, the vices not excepted; morally speaking, an easy-going man, he took the world as it came, and did not fancy himself a whit better than his fellows. Spenser was a Platonist, and fed his grave spirit on high speculations and moralities. Severe and chivalrous, dreaming of things to come, unsuppled by luxury, unenslaved by passion, somewhat scornful and self-sustained, it needed but a tyrannous king, an electrical political atmosphere, and a deeper interest in theology, to make a Puritan of him, as these things made a Puritan of Milton. The differences between Chaucer and

Spenser are seen at a glance in their portraits. Chaucer's face is round, good-humoured, constitutionally pensive, and thoughtful. You see in it that he has often been amused, and that he may easily be amused again. Spenser's is of sharper and keener feature, disdainful, and breathing that severity which appertains to so many of the Elizabethan men. A fourteenth-century child, with delicate prescience, would have asked Chaucer to assist her in a strait, and would not have been disappointed. A sixteenth-century child in like circumstances would have shrunk from drawing on herself the regards of the sterner-looking man. We can trace the descent of the Chaucerian face and genius in Shakspeare and Scott, of the Spenserian in Milton and Wordsworth. In our own day, Mr. Browning takes after Chaucer, Mr. Tennyson takes after Spenser.

Hazlitt, writing of the four great English poets, tells us, Chaucer's characteristic is intensity, Spenser's remoteness, Milton's sublimity, and Shakspeare's everything. The sentence is epigrammatic and memorable enough; but so far as Chaucer is concerned, it requires a little explanation. He is not intense, for instance, as Byron is intense, or as Wordsworth is intense. He does not see man like the one, nor nature like the other. He would not have cared much for either of these poets. And yet, so far as straight-forwardness in dealing with a subject, and complete though quiet realisation of it goes to make up intensity of poetic mood, Chaucer amply justifies his critic. There is no wastefulness or explosiveness about the old writer. He does his work silently, and with no appearance of effort. His poetry shines upon us like a May morning, but the streak over the eastern hill, the dew on the grass, the wind that bathes the brows of the wayfarer are not there by haphazard; they are the results of occult forces, a whole solar system has had a hand in their production. From the apparent ease with which an artist works, one does not readily give him credit for the mental force he is continuously putting forth. To many people a chaotic "Festus" is more wonderful than a rounded, melodious "Princess." The load which a strong man bears gracefully does not seem so heavy as the load which the weaker man staggers under. Incompletion is force fighting; completion is force quiescent, its work done. Nature's forces are patent enough in some scarred volcanic moon in which no creature can breathe; only the sage, in some soft green earth, can discover the same forces reft of fierceness and terror, and translated into sunshine and falling dew, and the rainbow gleaming on the shower. It is somewhat in this way that the propriety of Hazlitt's criticism is to be vindicated. Chaucer is the most simple, natural, and homely of our poets, and whatever he attempts he does thoroughly. The Wife of Bath is so distinctly limned that she could sit for her portrait. You can count the embroidered sprigs in the jerkin of the squire. You hear the pilgrims laugh as they ride to Canterbury. The whole thing is admirably life-like and seems easy, and in the seeming easiness we are apt to forget the imaginative sympathy which bodies forth the characters, and the joy and sorrow from which that sympathy has drawn nurture. Unseen by us the ore has been dug, and smelted in secret furnaces, and when it is poured into perfect moulds, we are apt to forget by what potency the whole thing has been brought about.

And, with his noticing eyes, into what a brilliant, many-tinted world was Chaucer born. In his day life had a certain breadth, colour, and picturesqueness which it does not possess now. It wore a braver dress, and flaunted more in the sun. Five centuries effect a great change on manners. A man may now-a-days, and without the slightest suspicion of the fact, brush clothes with half the English peerage on a sunny afternoon in Pall Mall. Then it was quite different. The fourteenth century loved magnificence and show. Great lords kept princely state in the country; and when they came abroad, what a retinue, what waving of plumes, and shaking of banners, and glittering of rich dresses! Religion was picturesque, with dignitaries and cathedrals, and fuming incense, and the Host carried through the streets. The franklin kept open house, the city merchant feasted kings, the outlaw roasted his venison beneath the greenwood tree. There was a gallant monarch and a gallant court. The eyes of the

Countess of Salisbury shed influence; Maid Marian laughed in Sherwood. London is already a considerable place, numbering, perhaps, two hundred thousand inhabitants, the houses clustering close and high along the river banks; and on the beautiful April nights the nightingales are singing round the suburban villages of Strand, Holborn, and Charing. It is rich withal; for after the battle of Poitiers, Harry Picard, wine-merchant and Lord Mayor, entertained in the city four kings—to wit, Edward king of England, John king of France, David king of Scotland, and the king of Cyprus—and the last-named potentate, slightly heated with Harry's wine, engaged him at dice, and being nearly ruined thereby, the honest wine-merchant returned the poor king his money, which was received with all thankfulness. There is great stir on a summer's morning in that Warwickshire castle—pawing of horses, tossing of bridles, clanking of spurs. The old lord climbs at last into his saddle, and rides off to court, his favourite falcon on his wrist, four squires in immediate attendance carrying his arms, and behind these stretches a merry cavalcade, on which the chestnuts shed their milky blossoms. In the absence of the old peer, young Hopeful spends his time as befits his rank and expectations. He grooms his steed, plays with his hawks, feeds his hounds, and labours diligently to acquire grace and dexterity in the use of arms. At noon the portcullis is lowered, and out shoots a brilliant array of ladies and gentlemen, and falconers with hawks. They bend their course to the river, over which a rainbow is rising from a shower. Yonder young lady is laughing at our stripling squire, who seems half angry, half pleased: they are lovers, depend upon it. A few years, and the merry beauty will have become a noble, gracious woman, and the young fellow, sitting by a watch-fire on the eve of Cressy, will wonder if she is thinking of him. But the river is already reached. Up flies the alarmed heron, his long blue legs trailing behind him; a hawk is let loose; the young lady's laugh has ceased, as with gloved hand shading fair forehead and sweet gray eye, she watches hawk and heron lessening in heaven. The Crusades are now over, but the religious fervour which inspired them lingered behind; so that, even in Chaucer's day, Christian kings, when their consciences were oppressed by a crime more than usually weighty, talked of making an effort before they died to wrest Jerusalem and the sepulchre of Christ from the grasp of the infidel. England had at this time several holy shrines, the most famous being that of Thomas à Becket at Canterbury, which attracted crowds of pilgrims. The devout travelled in large companies; and, in the May mornings, a merry sight it was, as, with infinite clatter and merriment, with bells, minstrels, and buffoons, they passed through thorp and village, bound for the tomb of St. Thomas. The pageant of events, which seems enchantment when chronicled by Froissart's splendid pen, was to Chaucer

contemporaneous incident: the chivalric richness
was the familiar and everyday dress of his time.
Into this princely element he was endued, and he
saw every side of it—the frieze as well as the cloth
of gold. In the "Canterbury Tales" the fourteenth
century murmurs, as the sea murmurs in the pink-
mouthed shells upon our mantelpieces.

Of his life we do not know much. In his youth
he studied law and disliked it—a circumstance
common enough in the lives of men of letters,
from his time to that of Shirley Brooks. How he
lived, what he did, when he was a student, we are
unable to discover. Only for a moment is the curtain lifted, and we behold, in the old, quaint
peaked and gabled Fleet Street of that day, Chaucer thrashing a Franciscan friar (friar's offence
unknown), for which amusement he was next
morning fined two shillings. History has preserved
this for us, but has forgotten all the rest of his
early life, and the chronology of all his poems.
What curious flies are sometimes found in the
historic amber! On Chaucer's own authority,
we know that he served under Edward III in his
French campaign, and that he for some time lay
in a French prison. On his return from captivity
he married; he was a valet in the king's household;
he was sent on an embassy to Genoa, and is supposed to have visited Petrarch, then resident at
Padua, and to have heard from his lips the story
of "Griselda"—a tradition which one would like
to believe. He had his share of the sweets and the

bitters of life. He enjoyed offices and gifts of wine, and he felt the pangs of poverty and the sickness of hope deferred. He was comptroller of the customs for wools; from which post he was dismissed—*why*, we know not, although one cannot help remembering that Edward made the writing out of the accounts in Chaucer's own hand the condition of his holding office, and having one's surmises. Foreign countries, strange manners, meetings with celebrated men, love of wife and children, and their deaths, freedom and captivity, the light of a king's smile and its withdrawal, furnished ample matter of meditation to his humane and thoughtful spirit. In his youth he wrote allegories, full of ladies and knights dwelling in impossible forests, and nursing impossible passions, but, in his declining years, when fortune had done all it could for him and all it could against him, he discarded these dreams, and betook himself to the actual stuff of human nature. Instead of the "Romance of the Rose," we have the "Canterbury Tales," and the first great English Poet. One likes to fancy Chaucer in his declining days, living at Woodstock, with his books about him, and where he could watch the daisies opening themselves at sunrise, shutting themselves at sunset, and composing his wonderful stories in which the fourteenth century lives— riding to battle in iron gear, hawking in embroidered jerkin and waving plume, sitting in rich and solemn feast, the monarch on the dais.

Chaucer's early poems have music and fancy,

they are full of a natural delight in sunshine and the greenness of foliage, but they have little human interest. They are allegories for the most part, more or less satisfactorily wrought out. The allegorical turn of thought, the delight in pageantry, the "clothing upon" of abstractions with human forms, flowered originally out of chivalry and the feudal times. Chaucer imported it from the French, and was proud of it in his early poems, as a young fellow of that day might be proud of his horse furniture, his attire, his waving plume. And the poetic fashion thus set retained its vitality for a long while—indeed, it was only thoroughly made an end of by the French Revolution, which made an end of so much else. About the last trace of its influence is to be found in Burns's sentimental correspondence with Mrs. M'Lehose, in which the lady is addressed as Clarinda, and the poet signs himself Sylvander. It was at best a mere beautiful gauze screen drawn between the poet and nature, and passion put his foot through it at once. After Chaucer's youth was over, he discarded somewhat scornfully these abstractions and shows of things. The "Flower and the Leaf" is a beautifully-tinted dream; the "Canterbury Tales" are as real as anything in Shakspeare or Burns. The ladies in the earlier poems dwell in forests, and wear coronals on their heads; the people in the "Tales" are engaged in the actual concerns of life, and you can see the splashes of mire upon their clothes. The separate poems which make up the "Canterbury Tales" were probably written at different periods, after youth was gone, and when he had fallen out of love with florid imagery and allegorical conceits; and we can fancy him, perhaps fallen on evil days and in retirement, anxious to gather up these loose efforts into one consummate whole. If of his flowers he would make a bouquet for posterity, it was of course necessary to procure a string to tie them together. These necessities, which ruin other men, are the fortunate chances of great poets. Then it was that the idea arose of a meeting of pilgrims at the Tabard in Southwark, of their riding to Canterbury, and of the different personages relating stories to beguile the tedium of the journey. The notion was a happy one, and the execution is superb. In those days, as we know, pilgrimages were of frequent occurrence; and in the motley group that congregated on such occasions, the painter of character had full scope. All conditions of people are comprised in the noisy band issuing from the courtyard of the Southwark inn on that May morning in the fourteenth century. Let us go nearer and have a look at them!

There is a grave and gentle knight, who has fought in many wars, and who has many a time hurled his adversary down in tournament before the eyes of all the ladies there, and who has taken the place of honour at many a mighty feast. There, riding beside him, is a blooming squire, his son, fresh as the month of May, singing day and night from very gladness of heart—an impetuous young fellow, who is looking forward to the time when he will flesh his maiden sword, and shout his first war-cry in a stricken field. There is an abbot mounted on a brown steed. He is middle-aged; his bald crown shines like glass, and his face looks as if it were anointed with oil. He has been a valiant trencherman at many a well-furnished feast. Above all things, he loves hunting; and when he rides, men can hear his bridle ringing in the whistling wind loud and clear as a chapel bell. There is a thin, ill-conditioned clerk, perched perilously on a steed as thin and ill-conditioned as himself. He will never be rich, I fear. He is a great student, and would rather have a few books bound in black and red hanging above his bed than be sheriff of the county. There is a prioress so gentle and tender-hearted, that she weeps if she hears the whimper of a beaten hound, or sees a mouse caught in a trap. There rides the laughing Wife of Bath, bold-faced and fair. She is an adept in love matters. Five husbands already "she has fried in their own grease" till they were glad to get into their graves to escape the scourge of her tongue—Heaven rest their souls, and swiftly send a sixth! She wears a hat large as a targe or buckler, brings the artillery of her eyes to bear on the young squire, and jokes him about his sweetheart. Beside her is a worthy parson, who delivers faithfully the message of his Master. Although he is poor, he gives away the half of his tithes in charity. His parish is waste and wide, yet, if sickness or misfortune should befall one of his flock, he rides in spite of wind, or rain, or thunder, to administer consolation. Among the crowd rides a rich franklin, who sits in the Guildhall on the dais. He is profuse and hospitable as summer. All day his table stands in the hall covered with meats and drinks, and every one who enters is welcome. There is a ship-man, whose beard has been shaken by many a tempest, whose cheek knows the kiss of the salt sea spray; a merchant, with a grave look, clean and neat in his attire, and with plenty of gold in his purse. There is a doctor of physic, who has killed more men than the knight, talking to a clerk of laws. There is a merry friar, a lover of good cheer; and when seated in a tavern among his companions, singing songs it would be scarcely decorous to repeat, you may see his eyes twinkling in his head for joy, like stars on a frosty night. Beside him is a ruby-faced Sompnour, whose breath stinks of garlic and onions; who is ever roaring for wine—strong wine, wine red as blood; and when drunk, he disdains English— nothing but Latin will serve his turn. In front of all is a miller, who has been drinking over-night, and is now but indifferently sober. There is not a door in the country that he cannot break by running at it with his head. The pilgrims are all ready, the host gives the word, and they defile through the arch. The miller blows his bagpipes as they issue from the town; and away they ride to Canterbury, through the boon sunshine, and between the white hedges of the English May.

Had Chaucer spent his whole life in seeking, he could not have selected a better contemporary circumstance for securing variety of character than a pilgrimage to Canterbury. It comprises, as we see, all kinds and conditions of people. It is the fourteenth-century England in little. In our time, the only thing that could match it in this respect is Epsom down on the great race-day. But then Epsom down is too unwieldy; the crowd is too great, and it does not cohere, save for the few seconds when the gay jackets are streaming towards the winning-post. The Prologue to the "Canterbury Tales," in which we make the acquaintance of the pilgrims, is the ripest, most genial, and humorous—altogether the most masterly thing which Chaucer has left us. In its own way, and within its own limits, it is the most wonderful thing in the language. The people we read about are as real as the people we brush clothes with in the street—nay, much *more* real, for we not only see their faces, and the fashion and texture of their garments, we know also what they think, how they express themselves, and with what eyes they look out on the world. Chaucer's art in this Prologue is simple perfection. He indulges in no irrelevant description; he airs no fine sentiments; he takes no special pains as to style or poetic ornament; but every careless touch tells—every sly line reveals character; the description of each man's horse-furniture and array reads like a memoir. The nun's pretty oath bewrays her.

We see the bold, well-favoured countenance of the
Wife of Bath beneath her hat, as "broad as a
buckler or a targe"; and the horse of the clerk,
"as lean as is a rake," tells tales of his master's
cheer. Our modern dress is worthless as an indi-
cation of the character, or even of the social rank,
of the wearer; in the olden time it was significant
of personal tastes and appetites, of profession,
and condition of life generally. See how Chaucer
brings out a character by touching merely on a few
points of attire and personal appearance:—

> *I saw his sleeves were purfil'd at the hand*
> *With fur, and that the finest of the land;*
> *And for to fasten his hood under his chin*
> *He had of gold y'wrought a curious pin.*
> *A love-knot in the greater end there was;*
> *His head was bald, and shone as any glass,*
> *And eke his face as if it was anoint.*

What more would you have? You could not have
known the monk better if you had lived all your
life in the monastery with him. The sleeves daintily
purfiled with fur give one side of him, the curious
pin with the love-knot another, and the shining
crown and face complete the character and the
picture. The sun itself could not photograph more
truly.

On their way the pilgrims tell tales, and these are
as various as their relaters; in fact, the Prologue
is the soil out of which they all grow. Dramatic

propriety is everywhere instinctively preserved.
"The Knight's Tale" is noble, splendid, and
chivalric as his own nature; the tale told by the
Wife of Bath is exactly what one would expect.
With what good humour the rosy sinner confesses
her sins! how hilarious she is in her repentance!
"The Miller's Tale" is coarse and full-flavoured,
just the kind of thing to be told by a rough humorous fellow who is hardly yet sober. And here it
may be said, that although there is a good deal
of coarseness in the "Canterbury Tales," there
is not the slightest tinge of pruriency. There is such
a single-heartedness and innocence in Chaucer's
vulgarest and broadest stories, such a keen eye for
humour, and such a hearty enjoyment of it, and
at the same time such an absence of any delight in
impurity for impurity's sake, that but little danger
can arise from their perusal. He is so fond of fun
that he will drink it out of a cup that is only indifferently clean. He writes often like Fielding, he
never writes as Smollett sometimes does. These
stories, ranging from the noble romance of Palamon and Arcite, to the rude intrigues of Clerk
Nicholas—the one fitted to draw tears down the
cheeks of noble ladies and gentlemen, the other
to convulse with laughter the midriffs of illiterate
clowns—give one an idea of the astonishing range
of Chaucer's powers. He can suit himself to every
company, make himself at home in every circumstance of life; can mingle in tournaments where
beauty is leaning from balconies, and the knights,

with spear in rest, wait for the blast of the trumpet; and he can with equal ease sit with a couple of drunken friars in a tavern laughing over the confessions they hear, and singing questionable catches between whiles. Chaucer's range is wide as that of Shakspeare—if we omit that side of Shakspeare's mind which confronts the other world, and out of which Hamlet sprang—and his men and women are even more real, and more easily matched in the living and breathing world. For in Shakspeare's characters, as in his language, there is surplusage, superabundance; the measure is heaped and running over. From his sheer wealth he is often the most *un*dramatic of writers. He is so frequently greater than his occasion, he has no small change to suit emergencies, and we have guineas in place of groats. Romeo is more than a mortal lover, and Mercutio more than a mortal wit; the kings in the Shakspearian world are more kingly than earthly sovereigns; Rosalind's laughter was never heard save in the forest of Arden. His madmen seem to have eaten of some "strange root." No such boon companion as Falstaff ever heard chimes at midnight. His very clowns are transcendental, with scraps of wisdom springing out of their foolishest speech. Chaucer, lacking Shakspeare's excess and prodigality of genius, could not so gloriously err, and his creations have a harder, drier, more realistic look; are more like the people we hear uttering ordinary English speech, and see on ordinary country

[229]

roads against an ordinary English sky. If need were, any one of them could drive pigs to market. Chaucer's characters are individual enough, their idiosyncrasies are sharply enough defined, but they are to some extent literal and prosaic; they are of the "earth, earthy"; out of his imagination no Ariel ever sprang, no half-human, half-brutish Caliban ever crept. He does not effloresce in illustrations and images, the flowers do not hide the grass; his pictures are masterpieces, but they are portraits, and the man is brought out by a multiplicity of short touches—caustic, satirical, and matter-of-fact. His poetry may be said to resemble an English country road, on which passengers of different degrees of rank are continually passing—now knight, now boor, now abbot: Spenser's, for instance, and all the more fanciful styles, to a tapestry on which a whole Olympus has been wrought. The figures on the tapestry are much the more noble-looking, it is true, but then they are dreams and phantoms, whereas the people on the country road actually exist.

The "Knight's Tale"—which is the first told on the way to Canterbury—is a chivalrous legend, full of hunting, battle, and tournament. Into it, although the scene is laid in Greece, Chaucer has, with a fine scorn of anachronism, poured all the splendour, colour, pomp, and circumstance of the fourteenth century. It is brilliant as a banner displayed to the sunlight. It is real cloth of gold. Compared with it, "Ivanhoe" is a spectacle at

Astley's. The style is everywhere more adorned than is usual, although even here, and in the richest parts, the short, homely, caustic Chaucerian line is largely employed. The "Man of Law's Tale," again, is distinguished by quite a different merit. It relates the sorrows and patience of Constance, and is filled with the beauty of holiness. Constance might have been sister to Cordelia: she is one of the white lilies of womanhood. Her story is almost the tenderest in our literature. And Chaucer's art comes out in this, that although she would spread her hair, nay, put her very heart beneath the feet of those who wrong her, we do not cease for one moment to respect her. This is a feat which has but seldom been achieved. It has long been a matter of reproach to Mr. Thackeray, for instance, that the only faculty with which he gifts his good women is a supreme faculty of tears. To draw any very high degree of female patience is one of the most difficult of tasks. If you represent a woman bearing wrong with a continuous unmurmuring meekness, presenting to blows, come from what quarter they may, nothing but a bent neck, and eyelids humbly drooped, you are in nine cases out of ten painting elaborately the portrait of a fool; and if you miss making her a fool, you are certain to make her a bore. Your patient woman, in books and life, does not draw on our gratitude. When her goodness is not stupidity— which it frequently is—it is insulting. She walks about an incarnate rebuke. Her silence is an in-

cessant complaint. A teacup thrown at your head
is not half so alarming as her meek, much-wronged,
unretorting face. You begin to suspect that she
consoles herself with the thought that there is
another world where brutal brothers and husbands
are settled with for their behaviour to their angelic
wives and sisters in this. Chaucer's Constance is
neither fool nor bore, although in the hands of
anybody else she would have been one or other,
or both. Like the holy religion which she sym-
bolises, her sweet face draws blessing and love
wherever it goes; it heals old wounds with its
beauty, it carries peace into the heart of discord,
it touches murder itself into soft and penitential
tears. In reading the old tender-hearted poet, we
feel that there is something in a woman's sweetness and forgiveness that the masculine mind
cannot fathom; and we adore the hushed step
and still countenance of Constance almost as if
an angel passed.

Chaucer's orthography is unquestionably uncouth at first sight; but it is not difficult to read,
if you keep a good glossary beside you for occasional reference, and are willing to undergo a little
trouble. The language is antique, but it is full of
antique flavour. Wine of excellent vintage originally, it has improved through all the years
it has been kept. A very little trouble on the
reader's part, in the reign of Anne, would have
made him as intelligible as Addison; a very little
more, in the reign of Queen Victoria, will make

him more intelligible than Mr. Browning. Yet somehow it has been a favourite idea with many poets that he required modernisation, and that they were the men to do it. Dryden, Pope, and Wordsworth have tried their hands on him. Wordsworth performed his work in a reverential enough spirit; but it may be doubted whether his efforts have brought the old poet a single new reader. Dryden and Pope did not translate or modernise Chaucer—they committed assault and battery upon him. They turned his exquisitely *naïve* humour into their own coarseness; they put *doubles entendre* into his mouth; they blurred his female faces—as a picture is blurred when the hand of a vandal is drawn over its yet wet colours—and they turned his natural descriptions into the natural descriptions of "Windsor Forest" and the "Fables." The grand old writer does not need translation or modernisation; but, perhaps, if it be done at all, it had better be done through the medium of prose. What is characteristic about him will be better reached in that way. For the benefit of younger readers, I subjoin short prose versions of two of the "Canterbury Tales"—a story-book than which the world does not possess a better. Listen, then, to the tale the Knight told as the pilgrims rode to Canterbury:—

"There was once, as old stories tell, a certain Duke Theseus, lord and governor of Athens. The same was a great warrior and conqueror of realms. He defeated the Amazons, and wedded the queen

of that country, Hypolita. After his marriage, the
duke, his wife, and his sister Emily, with all
their host, were riding towards Athens, when they
were aware that a company of ladies, clad in
black, were kneeling two by two on the highway,
wringing their hands, and filling the air with
lamentations. The duke, beholding this piteous
sight, reined in his steed, and inquired the reason
of their grief. Whereat one of the ladies, queen to
the slain king Capaneus, told him that at the
siege of Thebes (of which town they were), Creon,
the conqueror, had thrown the bodies of their
husbands in a heap, and would on no account
allow them to be buried, so that their limbs were
mangled by vultures and wild beasts. At the hearing of this great wrong, the duke started down
from his horse, took the ladies one by one in his
arms and comforted them, sent Hypolita and
Emily home, displayed his great white banner,
and immediately rode towards Thebes with his
host. Arriving at the city, he attacked it boldly,
slew the tyrant Creon with his own hand, tore
down the houses—wall, roof, and rafter—and
then gave the bodies to the weeping ladies that
they might be honourably interred. While search-
ing amongst the slain Thebans, two young knights
were found grievously wounded, and by the richness of their armour they were known to be of the
blood-royal. These young knights, Palamon and
Arcite by name, the duke carried to Athens, and
flung into perpetual prison. Here they lived year

by year in mourning and woe. It happened one May morning that Palamon, who by the clemency of his keeper was roaming about in an upper chamber, looked out and beheld Emily singing in the garden and gathering flowers. At the sight of the beautiful apparition he started and cried, 'Ha!' Arcite rose up, crying, 'Dear cousin, what is the matter?' when he too was stricken to the heart by the shaft of her beauty. Then the prisoners began to dispute as to which of them had the better right to love her. Palamon said that he had seen her first; Arcite said that in love each man fought for himself; and so they disputed day by day. Now it so happened that at this time the Duke Perotheus came to visit his old playfellow and friend Theseus, and at his intercession Arcite was liberated on the condition that on pain of death he should never again be found in the Athenian dominions. Then the two knights grieved in their hearts. 'What matters liberty!' said Arcite—'I am a banished man! Palamon in his dungeon is happier than I. He can see Emily, and be gladdened by her beauty!' 'Woe is me!' said Palamon, 'here must I remain in durance. Arcite is abroad; he may make sharp war on the Athenian border, and win Emily by the sword.' When Arcite returned to his native city, he became so thin and pale with sorrow that his friends scarcely knew him. One night the god Mercury appeared to him in a dream, and told him to return to Athens, for in that city destiny had shaped an end of his woes. He arose next morning and went. He entered as a menial into the service of the Duke Theseus, and in a short time was promoted to be page of the chamber to Emily the bright. Meanwhile, by the help of a friend, Palamon, who had drugged his jailor with spiced wine, made his escape, and, as morning began to dawn, he hid himself in a grove. That very morning Arcite had ridden from Athens to gather some green branches to do honour to the month of May, and entered the grove in which Palamon was concealed. When he had gathered his green branches, he sat down, and, after the manner of lovers (who have no constancy of spirits), he began to pour forth his sorrows to the empty air. Palamon, knowing his voice, started up with a white face—'False traitor, Arcite! now I have found thee. Thou hast deceived the Duke Theseus! I am the lover of Emily, and thy mortal foe! Had I a weapon, one of us should never leave this grove alive!' 'By God, who sitteth above!' cried the fierce Arcite, 'were it not that thou art sick and mad for love, I would slay thee here with my own hand! Meats, and drinks, and bedding I shall bring thee to-night, to-morrow swords and two suits of armour; take thou the better, leave me the worse, and then let us see who can win the lady.' 'Agreed,' said Palamon; and Arcite rode away in great fierce joy of heart. Next morning, at the crowing of the cock, Arcite placed two suits of armour before him on his horse, and rode toward the grove. When they met, the colour of their faces changed. Each thought, 'Here comes my mortal enemy; one of us must be dead.' Then friend-like, as if they had been brothers, they assisted each the other to rivet on the armour; that done, the great bright swords went to and fro, and they were soon standing ankle-deep in blood. That same morning the Duke Theseus, his wife, and Emily, went forth to hunt the hart with hound and horn, and, as destiny ordered it, the chase led them to the very grove in which the knights were fighting. Theseus, shading his eyes from the sunlight with his hand, saw them, and, spurring his horse between them, cried, 'What manner of men are ye, fighting here without judge or officer?' Whereupon Palamon said, 'I am that Palamon who has broken your prison; this is Arcite the banished man, who, by returning to Athens, has forfeited his head. Do with us as you list. I have no more to say.' 'You have condemned yourselves!' cried the Duke; 'by mighty Mars the red, both of you shall die!' Then Emily and the Queen fell at his feet, and with prayers and tears and white hands lifted up besought the lives of the young knights, which was soon granted. Theseus began to laugh when he thought of his own young days. 'What a mighty god is Love!' quoth he. 'Here are Palamon and Arcite fighting for my sister, while they know she can only marry one. Fight they ever so much, she cannot marry both. I therefore ordain that

both of you go away and return this day year,
each bringing with him a hundred knights, and let
the victor in solemn tournament have Emily for
wife.' Who was glad now but Palamon! who
sprang up for joy but Arcite!

"When the twelve months had nearly passed
away, there was in Athens a great noise of work-
men and hammers. The Duke was busy with
preparations. He built a large amphitheatre,
seated round and round, to hold thousands of
people. He erected also three temples—one for
Diana, one for Mars, one for Venus; how rich
these were, how full of paintings and images, the
tongue cannot tell! Never was such preparation
made in the world. At last the day arrived in
which the knights were to make their entrance
into the city. A noise of trumpets was heard, and
through the city rode Palamon and his train.
With him came Lycurgus, the King of Thrace.
He stood in a great car of gold, drawn by four
white bulls, and his face was like a griffin when
he looked about. Twenty or more hounds used
for hunting the lion and the bear ran about the
wheels of his car; at his back rode a hundred
lords, stern and stout. Another burst of trumpets,
and Arcite entered with his troop. By his side
rode Emetrius, the King of India, on a bay steed
covered with cloth of gold. His hair was yellow,
and glittered like the sun; when he looked upon
the people, they thought his face was like the face
of a lion; his voice was like the thunder of a

trumpet. He bore a white eagle on his wrist, and tame lions and leopards ran among the horses of his train. They came to the city on a Sunday morning, and the jousts were to begin on Monday. What pricking of squires backwards and forwards, what clanking of hammers, what baying of hounds, that day! At last it was noon of Monday. Theseus declared from his throne that no blood was to be shed—that they should take prisoners only, and that he who was once taken prisoner should on no account again mingle in the fray. Then the Duke, the Queen, Emily, and the rest, rode to the lists with trumpets and melody. They had no sooner taken their places than through the gate of Mars rode Arcite and his hundred, displaying a red banner. At the self-same moment Palamon and his company entered by the gate of Venus, with a banner white as milk. They were then arranged in two ranks, their names were called over, the gates were shut, the herald gave his cry, loud and clear rang the trumpet, and crash went the spears as if made of glass when the knights met in battle shock. There might you see a knight unhorsed, a second crushing his way through the press, armed with a mighty mace, a third hurt and taken prisoner. Many a time that day in the swaying battle did the two Thebans meet, and thrice were they unhorsed. At last, near the setting of the sun, when Palamon was fighting with Arcite, he was wounded by Emetrius, and the battle thickened at the place. Emetrius is thrown out of his saddle a spear's length. Lycurgus is overthrown, and rolls on the ground, horse and man; and Palamon is dragged by main force to the stake. Then Theseus rose up where he sat, and cried, 'Ho! no more; Arcite of Thebes hath won Emily!' at which the people shouted so loudly, that it almost seemed the mighty lists would fall. Arcite now put up his helmet, and, curvetting his horse through the open space, smiled to Emily, when a fire from Pluto started out of the earth; the horse shied, and his rider was thrown on his head on the ground. When he was lifted, his breast was broken, and his face was as black as coal. Then there was grief in Athens—every one wept. Soon after, Arcite, feeling the cold death creeping up from his feet and darkening his face and eyes, called Palamon and Emily to his bedside, when he joined their hands, and died. The dead body was laid on a pile, dressed in splendid war-gear, his naked sword was placed by his side, the pile was heaped with gums, frankincense, and odours; a torch was applied, and when the flames rose up, and the smoky fragrance rolled to heaven, the Greeks galloped round three times, with a great shouting and clashing of shields."

The Man of Law's tale runs in this wise:—

"There dwelt in Syria once a company of merchants, who scented every land with their spices. They dealt in jewels, and cloth of gold, and sheeny satins. It so happened, that while some of them were dwelling in Rome for traffic, the people talked of nothing save the wonderful beauty of Constance, the daughter of the emperor. She was so fair, that every one who looked upon her face fell in love with her. In a short time the ships of the merchants, laden with rich wares, were furrowing the green sea going home. When they came to their native city, they could talk of nothing but the marvellous beauty of Constance. Their words being reported to the Sultan, he determined that none other should be his wife; and for this purpose he abandoned the religion of the false Prophet, and was baptized in the Christian faith. Ambassadors passed between the courts, and the day came at length when Constance was to leave Rome for her husband's palace in Syria. What kisses and tears and lingering embraces! What blessings on the little golden head which was so soon to lie in the bosom of a stranger! What state and solemnity in the procession which wound down from the shore to the ship! At last it was Syria. Crowds of people were standing on the beach. The mother of the Sultan was there; and when Constance stepped ashore, she took her in her arms and kissed her as if she had been her own child. Soon after, with trumpets and melody, and the trampling of innumerable horses, the Sultan came. Everything was joy and happiness. But the smiling demoness, his mother, could not forgive him for changing his faith, and she resolved to slay him that very night, and seize the government of the kingdom. He and all his lords were

stabbed in the rich hall while they were sitting
at their wine. Constance alone escaped. She was
then put into a ship alone, with food and clothes,
and told that she might find her way back to
Italy. She sailed away, and was never seen by
that people. For five years she wandered to and
fro upon the sea. Do you ask who preserved her?
The same God who fed Elijah with ravens, and
saved Daniel in the horrible den. At last she floated
into the English seas, and was thrown by the
waves on the Northumberland shore, near which
stood a great castle. The constable of the castle
came down in the morning to see the woeful woman. She spoke a kind of corrupt Latin, and could
neither tell her name nor the name of the country
of which she was a native. She said she was so
bewildered in the sea that she remembered nothing. The man could not help loving her, and so
took her home to live with himself and his wife.
Now, through the example and teaching of Constance, Dame Hermigild was converted to Christianity. It happened also that three aged Christian
Britons were living near that place in great fear
of their pagan neighbours, and one of these men
was blind. One day, as the constable, his wife,
and Constance were walking along the seashore,
they were met by the blind man, who called out,
'In the name of Christ, give me my sight, Dame
Hermigild!' At this, on account of her husband,
she was sore afraid, but, encouraged by Constance,
she wrought a great miracle, and gave the blind

man his sight. But Satan, the enemy of all, wanted to destroy Constance, and he employed a young knight for that purpose. This knight had loved her with a foul affection, to which she could give no return. At last, wild for revenge, he crept at night into Hermigild's chamber, slew her, and laid the bloody knife on the innocent pillow of Constance. The next morning there was woe and dolour in the house. She was brought before Alla, the king, charged with the murder. The people could not believe that she had done this thing— they knew she loved Hermigild so. Constance fell down on her knees and prayed to God for succour. Have you ever been in a crowd in which a man is being led to death, and, seeing a wild, pale face, know by that sign that you are looking upon the doomed creature?—so wild, so pale looked Constance when she stood before the king and people. The tears ran down Alla's face. 'Go fetch a book,' cried he; 'and if this knight swears that the woman is guilty, she shall surely die.' The book was brought, the knight took the oath, and that moment an unseen hand smote him on the neck, so that he fell down on the floor, his eyes bursting out of his head. Then a celestial voice was heard in the midst, crying, 'Thou hast slandered a daughter of Holy Church in high presence, and yet I hold my peace.' A great awe fell on all who heard, and the king and multitudes of his people were converted. Shortly after this, Alla wedded Constance with great richness and solemnity. At length he was called to defend his border against the predatory Scots, and in his absence a man-child was born. A messenger was sent with the blissful tidings to the king's camp; but, on his way, the messenger turned aside to the dwelling of Donegild, the king's mother, and said, 'Be blithe, madam; the queen has given birth to a son, and joy is in the land. Here is the letter I bear to the king.' The wicked Donegild said, 'You must be already tired—here are refreshments.' And while the simple man drank ale and wine, she forged a letter, saying that the queen had been delivered of a creature so fiendish and horrible, that no one in the castle could bear to look upon it. This letter the messenger gave to the king, and who can tell his grief! But he wrote in reply, 'Welcome be the child that Christ sends! Welcome, O Lord, be Thy pleasure! Be careful of my wife and child till my return.' The messenger on his return slept at Donegild's court, with the letter under his girdle. It was stolen while in his drunken sleep, and another put in its place, charging the constable not to let Constance remain three days in the kingdom, but to send her and her child away in the same ship in which she had come. The constable could not help himself. Thousands are gathered on the shore. With a face wild and pale as when she came from the sea, and bearing her crying infant in her arms, she comes through the crowd, which shrinks back, leaving a lane for her sorrow. She takes her seat in the little boat; and while the cruel people gaze hour by hour from the shore, she passes into the sunset, and away out into the night under the stars. When Alla returned from the war, and found how he had been deceived, he slew his mother in the bitterness of his heart.

"News had come to Rome of the cruelty of the Sultan's mother to Constance, and an army was sent to waste her country. After the land had been burned and desolated, the commander was crossing the seas in triumph, when he met the ship sailing in which sat Constance and her little boy. They were both brought to Rome, and although the commander's wife and Constance were cousins, the one did not know the other. By this time, remorse for the slaying of his mother had seized Alla's mind, and he could find no rest. He resolved to make a pilgrimage to Rome in search of peace. He crossed the Alps with his train, and entered the city with great glory and magnificence. One day he feasted at the commander's house, at which Constance dwelt; and at her request her little son was admitted, and during the progress of the feast the child went and stood looking in the king's face. 'What fair child is that standing yonder?' said the king. 'By St. John, I know not!' quoth the commander; 'he has a mother, but no father, that I know of.' And then he told the king— who seemed all the while like a man stunned— how he had found the mother and child floating about on the sea. The king rose from the table and sent for Constance, and when he saw her and thought on all her wrongs, he could not refrain from tears. 'This is your little son, Maurice,' she said, as she led him in by the hand. Next day she met the emperor her father in the street, and falling down on her knees before him, said, 'Father, has the remembrance of your young child Constance gone out of your mind? I am that Constance, whom you sent to Syria, and who was thought to be lost in the sea.' That day there was great joy in Rome; and soon afterwards, Alla, with his wife and child, returned to England, where they lived in great prosperity till he died."

BOOKS AND GARDENS

MOST men seek solitude from wounded vanity, from disappointed ambition, from a miscarriage in the passions; but some others from native instinct, as a duckling seeks water. I have taken to my solitude, such as it is, from an indolent turn of mind; and this solitude I sweeten by an imaginative sympathy which recreates the past for me—the past of the world, as well as the past which belongs to me as an individual—and which makes me independent of the passing moment. I see every one struggling after the unattainable, but I struggle not, and so spare myself the pangs of disappointment and disgust. I have no ventures at sea, and, consequently, do not fear the arrival of evil tidings. I have no desire to act any prominent part in the world, but I am devoured by an unappeasable curiosity as to the men who do act. I am not an actor, I am a spectator only. My sole occupation is sight-seeing. In a certain imperial idleness, I amuse myself with the world. Ambition! What do I care for ambition? The oyster with much pain produces its pearl. I take the pearl. Why should I produce one after this miserable, painful fashion? It would be but a flawed one at best. These pearls I can pick up by the dozen. The production of them is going on all around me, and there will be a nice crop for the solitary man of the next century. Look at a certain silent emperor, for instance; a hundred years hence *his* pearl will be handed about from hand to hand; will be curiously scrutinised and valued; will be set in its place in the world's cabinet. I confess I should like to see the completion of that filmy orb. Will it be pure in colour? Will its purity be marred by an ominous bloody streak? Of this I am certain, that in the cabinet in which the world keeps these peculiar treasures, no one will be looked at more frequently, or will provoke a greater variety of opinions as to its intrinsic worth.[1] Why should I be ambitious? Shall I write verses? I am not likely to surpass Mr. Tennyson or Mr. Browning in that walk. Shall I be a musician? The blackbird singing this moment somewhere in my garden-shrubbery puts me to instant shame. Shall I paint? The intensest scarlet on an artist's palette is but ochre to that I saw this morning at sunrise. No, no; let me enjoy Mr. Tennyson's verse, and the blackbird's song, and the colours of sunrise, but do not let me emulate them. I am happier as it is. I

[1]Subsequent history has not ratified Alexander Smith's interest in Napoleon III, who is almost forgotten in the perspective of a "bloody streak" still more terrible. But Smith evidently had forebodings of the Franco-Prussian War.—C. M.

do not need to make history—there are plenty of people willing to save me trouble on that score. The cook makes the dinner, the guest eats it, and the last, not without reason, is considered the happier man.

In my garden I spend my days; in my library I spend my nights. My interests are divided between my geraniums and my books. With the flower I am in the present; with the book I am in the past. I go into my library, and all history unrolls before me. I breathe the morning air of the world while the scent of Eden's roses yet lingered in it, while it vibrated only to the world's first brood of nightingales, and to the laugh of Eve. I see the pyramids building; I hear the shoutings of the armies of Alexander; I feel the ground shake beneath the march of Cambyses. I sit as in a theatre —the stage is time, the play is the play of the world. What a spectacle it is! What kingly pomp, what processions file past, what cities burn to heaven, what crowds of captives are dragged at the chariot-wheels of conquerors! I hear or cry "Bravo" when the great actors come on shaking the stage. I am a Roman emperor when I look at a Roman coin. I lift Homer, and I shout with Achilles in the trenches. The silence of the un-peopled Syrian plains, the out-comings and in-goings of the patriarchs, Abraham and Ishmael, Isaac in the fields at even-tide, Rebekah at the well, Jacob's guile. Esau's face reddened by desert sun-heat, Joseph's splendid funeral procession—

all these things I find within the boards of my Old Testament. What a silence in those old books as of a half-peopled world—what bleating of flocks—what green pastoral rest—what indubitable human existence! Across brawling centuries of blood and war, I hear the bleating of Abraham's flocks, the tinkling of the bells of Rebekah's camels. O men and women, so far separated yet so near, so strange yet so well known, by what miraculous power do I know ye all! Books are the true Elysian fields where the spirits of the dead converse, and into these fields a mortal may venture unappalled. What king's court can boast such company? What school of philosophy such wisdom? The wit of the ancient world is glancing and flashing there. There is Pan's pipe, there are the songs of Apollo. Seated in my library at night, and looking on the silent faces of my books, I am occasionally visited by a strange sense of the supernatural. They are not collections of printed pages, they are ghosts. I take one down and it speaks with me in a tongue not now heard on earth, and of men and things of which it alone possesses knowledge. I call myself a solitary, but sometimes I think I misapply the term. No man sees more company than I do. I travel with mightier cohorts around me than ever did Timour or Genghis Khan on their fiery marches. I am a sovereign in my library, but it is the dead, not the living, that attend my levees.

The house I dwell in stands apart from the little

town, and relates itself to the houses as I do to
the inhabitants. It sees everything, but is itself
unseen, or, at all events, unregarded. My study-
window looks down upon Dreamthorp like a meditative eye. Without meaning it, I feel I am a spy
on the ongoings of the quiet place. Around my
house there is an old-fashioned rambling garden,
with close-shaven grassy plots, and fantastically-
clipped yews, which have gathered their darkness
from a hundred summers and winters; and sun-
dials, in which the sun is constantly telling his
age; and statues, green with neglect and the
stains of the weather. The garden I love more
than any place on earth; it is a better study than
the room inside the house which is dignified by
that name. I like to pace its gravelled walks, to
sit in the moss-house, which is warm and cozy as
a bird's nest, and wherein twilight dwells at noon-
day; to enjoy the feast of colour spread for me in
the curiously-shaped floral spaces. My garden,
with its silence and the pulses of fragrance that
come and go on the airy undulations, affects me
like sweet music. Care stops at the gates, and
gazes at me wistfully through the bars. Among
my flowers and trees nature takes me into her own
hands, and I breathe freely as the first man. It
is curious, pathetic almost, I sometimes think,
how deeply seated in the human heart is the liking
for gardens and gardening. The sickly seamstress
in the narrow city lane tends her box of sicklier
mignonette. The retired merchant is as fond of

tulips as ever was Dutchman during the famous mania. The author finds a garden the best place to think out his thought. In the disabled statesman every restless throb of regret or ambition is stilled when he looks upon his blossomed appletrees. Is the fancy too far brought, that this love for gardens is a reminiscence haunting the race of that remote time in the world's dawn when but two persons existed—a gardener named Adam, and a gardener's wife called Eve?

When I walk out of my house into my garden I walk out of my habitual self, my every-day thoughts, my customariness of joy or sorrow by which I recognise and assure myself of my own identity. These I leave behind me for a time as the bather leaves his garments on the beach. This piece of garden-ground, in extent barely a square acre, is a kingdom with its own interests, annals, and incidents. Something is always happening in it. To-day is always different from yesterday. This spring a chaffinch built a nest in one of my yew-trees. The particular yew which the bird did me the honour to select had been clipped long ago into a similitude of Adam, and, in fact, went by his name. The resemblance to a human figure was, of course, remote, but the intention was evident. In the black shock head of our first parent did the birds establish their habitation. A prettier, rounder, more comfortable nest I never saw, and many a wild swing it got when Adam bent his back, and bobbed and shook his head when the bitter east wind was blowing. The nest interested me, and I visited it every day from the time that the first stained turquoise sphere was laid in the warm lining of moss and horsehair, till, when I chirped, four red hungry throats, eager for worm or slug, opened out of a confused mass of feathery down. What a hungry brood it was, to be sure, and how often father and mother were put to it to provide them sustenance! I went but the other day to have a peep, and, behold, brood and parent-birds were gone, the nest was empty, Adam's visitors had departed. In the corners of my bedroom window I have a couple of swallows' nests, and nothing can be pleasanter in these summer mornings than to lie in a kind of half-dream, conscious all the time of the chatterings and endearments of the man-loving creatures. They are beautifully restless, and are continually darting around their nests in the window-corners. All at once there is a great twittering and noise; something of moment has been witnessed, something of importance has occurred in swallow-world, perhaps a fly of unusual size or savour has been bolted. Clinging with their feet, and with their heads turned charmingly aside, they chatter away with voluble sweetness, then with a gleam of silver they are gone, and in a trice one is poising itself in the wind above my tree-tops, while the other dips her wing as she darts after a fly through the arches of the bridge which lets the slow stream down to the sea. I

go to the southern wall, against which I have
trained my fruit-trees, and find it a sheet of white
and vermeil blossom, and as I know it by heart,
I can notice what changes take place on it day by
day, what later clumps of buds have burst into
colour and odour. What beauty in that blooming
wall—the wedding-presents of a princess ranged
for admiration would not please me half so much;
what delicate colouring, what fragrance the thiev-
ish winds steal from it without making it one
odour the poorer, with what a complacent hum
the bee goes past! My chaffinch's nest, my swallows—twittering but a few months ago around the
kraal of the Hottentot, or chasing flies around the
six solitary pillars of Baalbec—with their nests
in the corners of my bedroom windows, my long-
armed fruit-trees flowering against my sunny wall
are not mighty pleasures, but then they are my
own, and I have not to go in search of them. And
so, like a wise man, I am content with what I
have, and make it richer by my fancy, which is
as cheap as sunlight, and gilds objects quite as
prettily. It is the coins in my own pocket, not the
coins in the pockets of my neighbour, that are of
use to me. Discontent has never a doit in her
purse, and envy is the most poverty-stricken of
the passions.

His own children, and the children he happens
to meet on the country road, a man regards with
quite different eyes. The strange, sunburnt brats
returning from a primrose-hunt and laden with

floral spoils, may be as healthy-looking, as pretty, as well-behaved, as sweet-tempered, as neatly dressed as those that bear his name—may be in every respect as worthy of love and admiration, but then they have the misfortune not to belong to him. That little fact makes a great difference. He knows nothing about them, his acquaintance with them is born and dead in a moment. I like my garden better than any other garden for the same reason. It is my own. And ownership in such a matter implies a great deal. When I first settled here, the ground around the house was sour moorland. I made the walk, planted the trees, built the moss-house, erected the sun-dial, brought home the rhododendrons and fed them with the mould which they love so well. I am the creator of every blossom, of every odour that comes and goes in the wind. The rustle of my trees is to my ear what his child's voice is to my friends the village doctor or the village clergyman. I know the genealogy of every tree and plant in my garden. I watch their growth as a father watches the growth of his children. It is curious enough, as shewing from what sources objects derive their importance, that if you have once planted a tree for other than mere commercial purposes—and in that case it is usually done by your orders and by the hands of hirelings—you have always in it a quite peculiar interest. You care more for it than you care for all the forests of Norway or America. *You* have planted it, and that is sufficient to make it peculiar amongst the trees of the world. This personal interest I take in every inmate of my garden, and this interest I have increased by sedulous watching. But really trees and plants resemble human beings in many ways. You shake a packet of seed into your forcing-frame, and while some grow, others pine and die, or struggle on under hereditary defect, shewing indifferent blossoms late in the season, and succumb at length. So far as one could discover, the seeds were originally alike—they received the same care, they were fed by the same moisture and sunlight, but of no two of them are the issues the same. Do I not see something of this kind in the world of men, and can I not please myself with quaint analogies? These plants and trees have their seasons of illness, and their sudden deaths. Your best rose-tree, whose fame has spread for twenty miles, is smitten by some fell disease; its leaves take an unhealthy hue, and in a day or so it is sapless—dead. A tree of mine, the first last spring to put out its leaves, and which wore them till November, made this spring no green response to the call of the sunshine. Marvelling what ailed it, I went to examine, and found it had been dead for months—and yet during the winter there had been no frost to speak of, and more than its brothers and sisters it was in no way exposed. These are the tragedies of the garden, and they shadow forth other tragedies nearer us. In everything we find a kind of dim mirror of ourselves. Sterne, if placed in a desert, said he would love a tree; and I can fancy such a love would not be altogether unsatisfying. Love of trees and plants is safe. You do not run risk in your affections. They are my children, silent and beautiful, untouched by any passion, unpolluted by evil tempers; for me they leaf and flower themselves. In autumn they put off their rich apparel, but next year they are back again with dresses fair as ever; and—one can extract a kind of fanciful bitterness from the thought—should I be laid in my grave in winter, they would all in spring be back again with faces as bright and with breaths as sweet, missing me not at all. Ungrateful, the one I am fondest of would blossom very prettily if planted on the soil that covers me —where my dog would die, where my best friend would perhaps raise an inscription!

I like flowering plants, but I like trees more, for the reason, I suppose, that they are slower in coming to maturity, are longer-lived, that you can become better acquainted with them, and that in the course of years memories and associations hang as thickly on their boughs as do leaves in summer or fruits in autumn. I do not wonder that great earls value their trees, and never, save in direst extremity, lift upon them the axe. Ancient descent and glory are made audible in the proud murmur of immemorial woods. There are forests in England whose leafy noises may be shaped into Agincourt and the names of the battlefields of

the Roses; oaks that dropped their acorns in the
year that Henry VIII held his Field of the Cloth
of Gold, and beeches that gave shelter to the deer
when Shakspeare was a boy. There they stand,
in sun and shower, the broad-armed witnesses of
perished centuries; and sore must his need be
who commands a woodland massacre. A great
English tree, the rings of a century in its bole, is
one of the noblest of natural objects; and it
touches the imagination no less than the eye, for
it grows out of tradition and a past order of things,
and is pathetic with the suggestions of dead generations. Trees waving a colony of rooks in the wind
to-day, are older than historic lines. Trees are
your best antiques. There are cedars on Lebanon
which the axes of Solomon spared, they say, when
he was busy with his Temple; there are olives on
Olivet that might have rustled in the ears of the
Master and the Twelve; there are oaks in Sherwood which have tingled to the horn of Robin
Hood and have listened to Maid Marian's laugh.
Think of an existing Syrian cedar which is nearly
as old as history, which was middle-aged before
the wolf suckled Romulus; think of an existing
English elm in whose branches the heron was
reared which the hawks of Saxon Harold killed!
If you are a notable, and wish to be remembered,
better plant a tree than build a city or strike a
medal—it will outlast both.

My trees are young enough, and if they do not
take me away into the past, they project me into

the future. When I planted them, I knew I was performing an act, the issues of which would outlast me long. My oaks are but saplings; but what undreamed-of English kings will they not outlive? I pluck my apples, my pears, my plums; and I know that from the same branches other hands will pluck apples, pears, and plums when this body of mine will have shrunk into a pinch of dust. I cannot dream with what year these hands will date their letters. A man does not plant a tree for himself, he plants it for posterity. And sitting idly in the sunshine, I think at times of the unborn people who will, to some small extent, be indebted to me. Remember me kindly, ye future men and women! When I am dead, the juice of my apples will foam and spirt in your cider presses, my plums will gather for you their misty bloom; and that any of your youngsters should be choked by one of my cherry-stones, merciful Heaven forfend!

In this pleasant summer weather I hold my audience in my garden rather than in my house. In all my interviews the sun is a third party. Every village has its Fool, and, of course, Dreamthorp is not without one. Him I get to run my messages for me, and he occasionally turns my garden borders with a neat hand enough. He and I hold frequent converse, and people here, I have been told, think we have certain points of sympathy. Although this is not meant for a compliment, I take it for one. The poor, faithful creature's brain has strange visitors: now 'tis fun, now wisdom, and now something which seems in the queerest way a compound of both. He lives in a kind of twilight which observes objects, and his remarks seem to come from another world than that in which ordinary people live. He is the only original person of my acquaintance; his views of life are his own, and form a singular commentary on those generally accepted. He is dull enough at times, poor fellow; but anon he startles you with something, and you think he must have wandered out of Shakspeare's plays into this out-of-the-way place. Up from the village now and then comes to visit me the tall, gaunt, atrabilious confectioner, who has a hankering after Red-republicanism, and the destruction of Queen, Lords, and Commons. Guy Fawkes is, I believe, the only martyr in his calendar. The sourest-tempered man, I think, that ever engaged in the manufacture of sweetmeats. I wonder that the oddity of the thing never strikes himself. To be at all consistent, he should put poison in his lozenges, and become the Herod of the village innocents. One of his many eccentricities is a love for flowers, and he visits me often to have a look at my greenhouse and my borders. I listen to his truculent and revolutionary speeches, and take my revenge by sending the gloomy egotist away with a nosegay in his hand, and a gay-coloured flower stuck in a button-hole. He goes quite unconscious of my floral satire.

The village clergyman and the village doctor are great friends of mine; they come to visit me often, and smoke a pipe with me in my garden. The twain love and respect each other, but they regard the world from different points of view, and I am now and again made witness of a good-humoured passage of arms. The clergyman is old, unmarried, and a humorist. His sallies and his gentle eccentricities seldom provoke laughter, but they are continually awakening the pleasantest smiles. Perhaps what he has seen of the world, its sins, its sorrows, its death-beds, its widows and orphans, has tamed his spirit, and put a tenderness into his wit. I do not think I have ever encountered a man who so adorns his sacred profession. His pious, devout nature produces sermons just as naturally as my apple-trees produce apples. He is a tree that flowers every Sunday. Very beautiful is his reverence for the Book, his trust in it; through long acquaintance, its ideas have come to colour his entire thought, and you come upon its phrases in his ordinary speech. He is more himself in the pulpit than anywhere else, and you get nearer him in his sermons than you do sitting with him at his tea-table, or walking with him on the country roads. He does not feel confined in his orthodoxy; in it he is free as a bird in the air. The doctor is, I conceive, as good a Christian as the clergyman, but he is impatient of pale or limit; he never comes to a fence without feeling a desire to get over it. He is a great hunter

of insects, and he thinks that the wings of his
butterflies might yield very excellent texts; he is
fond of geology, and cannot, especially when he is
in the company of the clergyman, resist the temptation of hurling a fossil at Moses. He wears his
scepticism as a coquette wears her ribbons—to
annoy if he cannot subdue—and when his purpose
is served, he puts his scepticism aside—as the
coquette puts her ribbons. Great arguments arise
between them, and the doctor loses his field
through his loss of temper, which, however, he
regains before any harm is done. For the worthy
man is irascible withal, and opposition draws
fire from him.

After an outburst, there is a truce between the
friends for a while, till it is broken by theological
battle over the age of the world, or some other the
like remote matter, which seems important to me
only in so far as it affords ground for disputation.
These truces are broken sometimes by the doctor,
sometimes by the clergyman. T'other evening
the doctor and myself were sitting in the garden,
smoking each a meditative pipe. Dreamthorp lay
below, with its old castle and its lake, and its
hundred wreaths of smoke floating upward into
the sunset. Where we sat the voices of children
playing in the street could hardly reach us. Suddenly a step was heard on the gravel, and the
next moment the clergyman appeared, as it
seemed to me with a peculiar airiness of aspect,
and the light of a humorous satisfaction in his

eye. After the usual salutations he took his seat beside us, lifted a pipe of the kind called "church-warden" from the box on the ground, filled and lighted it, and for a little while we were silent all three. The clergyman then drew an old magazine from his side pocket, opened it at a place where the leaf had been carefully turned down, and drew my attention to a short poem, which had for its title, "Vanity Fair," imprinted in German text. This poem he desired me to read aloud. Laying down my pipe carefully beside me, I complied with his request. It ran thus, for as after my friends went it was left behind, I have written it down word for word:—

The world-old Fair of Vanity
  Since Bunyan's day has grown discreeter;
No more it flocks in crowds to see
  A blazing Paul or Peter.

Not that a single inch it swerves
  From hate of saint, or love of sinner;
But martyrs shock aesthetic nerves,
  And spoil the goût of dinner.

Raise but a shout, or flaunt a scarf—
  Its mobs are all agog and flying;
They'll cram the levee of a dwarf,
  And leave a Haydon dying.

[263]

DREAMTHORP

They live upon each newest thing,
    They fill their idle days with seeing;
Fresh news of courtier and of king
    Sustains their empty being.

The ₊tatelier, from year to year,
    Maintain their comfortable stations
At the wide windows that o'erpeer
    The public square of nations;

While through it heaves, with cheers and groans,
    Harsh drums of battle in the distance,
Frightful with gallows, ropes, and thrones,
    The medley of existence;

Amongst them tongues are wagging much:
    Hark to the philosophic sisters!
To his, whose keen satiric touch,
    Like the Medusa, blisters!

All things are made for talk—St. Paul—
    The pattern of an altar cushion—
A Paris wild with carnival,
    Or red with revolution.

And much they knew, that sneering crew,
    Of things above the world and under:
They search'd the hoary deep; they knew
    The secret of the thunder;

BOOKS AND GARDENS

The pure white arrow of the light
  They split into its colours seven;
They weigh'd the sun; they dwelt, like night,
  Among the stars of heaven;

They've found out life and death—the first
  Is known but to the upper classes—
The second, pooh! 'tis at the worst
  A dissolution into gases.

And vice and virtue are akin
  As black and white from Adam issue—
One flesh, one blood, though sheeted in
  A different-colour'd tissue.

Their science groped from star to star,
  But than herself found nothing greater—
What wonder? in a Leyden jar
  They bottled the Creator.

Fires flutter'd on their lightning-rod;
  They clear'd the human mind from error;
They emptied heaven of its God,
  And Tophet of its terror.

Better the savage in his dance
  Than these acute and syllogistic!
Better a reverent ignorance
  Than knowledge atheistic!

Have they dispell'd one cloud that lowers
So darkly on the human creature?
They with their irreligious powers
Have subjugated nature.

But as a satyr wins the charms
Of maiden in a forest hearted,
He finds, when clasp'd within his arms,
The outraged soul departed.

When I had done reading these verses, the clergyman glanced slyly along to see the effect of his shot. The doctor drew two or three hurried whiffs, gave a huge grunt of scorn, then turning sharply, asked, "What is 'a reverent ignorance'? What is 'a knowledge atheistic'?" The clergyman, skewered by the sudden question, wriggled a little, and then began to explain—with no great heart, however, for he had had his little joke out, and did not care to carry it further. The doctor listened for a little, and then, laying down his pipe, said with some heat, "It won't do. 'Reverent ignorance' and such trash is a mere jingle of words: *that* you know as well as I. You stumbled on these verses, and brought them up here to throw them at me. They don't harm me in the least, I can assure you. There is no use," continued the doctor, mollifying at the sight of his friend's countenance, and seeing how the land lay—"there is no use speaking on such matters to our incurious, solitary friend here, who could bask comfortably in sunshine for a century, without once inquiring whence came the light and heat. But let me tell you," lifting his pipe and shaking it across me at the clergyman, "that science has done services to your cloth which have not always received the most grateful acknowledgments. Why, man," here he began to fill his pipe slowly, "the theologian and the man of science, although they seem to diverge and lose sight of each other, are all the while working to one end. Two exploring parties in Australia set out from one point; the one goes east and the other west. They lose sight of each other—they know nothing of one another's whereabouts—but they are all steering to one point"—the sharp spurt of a fusee on the garden-seat came in here, followed by an aromatic flavour in the air—"and when they do meet, which they are certain to do in the long run"—here the doctor put the pipe in his mouth, and finished his speech with it there—"the figure of the continent has become known, and may be set down in maps. The exploring parties have started long ago. What folly in the one to pooh-pooh, or be suspicious of the exertions of the other! That party deserves the greatest credit which meets the other more than half way."—"Bravo!" cried the clergyman, when the doctor had finished his oration; "I don't know that I could fill your place at the bed-side, but I am quite sure that you could fill mine in the pulpit."—"I am not sure that the congregation would approve of the change—I might disturb their slumbers"; and, pleased with his retort, his cheery laugh rose through a cloud of smoke into the sunset.

Heigho! mine is a dull life, I fear, when this little affair of the doctor and the clergyman takes the dignity of an incident, and seems worthy of being recorded.

The doctor was anxious that, during the following winter, a short course of lectures should be delivered in the village schoolroom, and in my garden he held several conferences on the matter with the clergyman and myself. It was arranged finally that the lectures should be delivered, and that one of them should be delivered by me. I need not say how pleasant was the writing out of my discourse, and how the pleasure was heightened by the slightest thrill of alarm at my own temerity. My lecture I copied out in my most careful hand, and, as I had it by heart, I used to declaim passages of it ensconced in my moss-house, or concealed behind my shrubbery trees. In these places I tried it all over sentence by sentence. The evening came at last which had been looked forward to for a couple of months or more. The small schoolroom was filled by forms on which the people sat, and a small reading-desk, with a tumbler of water on it, at the further end, waited for me. When I took my seat, the couple of hundred eyes struck into me a certain awe. I discovered in a moment why the orator of the hustings is so deferential to the mob. You may despise every individual member of your audience, but these despised individuals, in their capacity of a collective body, overpower you. I addressed the people with the most unfeigned respect. When I began, too, I found what a dreadful thing it is to hear your own voice inhabiting the silence. You are related to your voice, and yet divorced from it. It is you, and yet a thing apart. All the time it is going on, you can be critical as to its tone, volume, cadence, and other qualities, as if it was the voice of a stranger. Gradually, however, I got accustomed to my voice, and the respect which I entertained for my hearers so far relaxed that I was at last able to look them in the face. I saw the doctor and the clergyman smile encouragingly, and my half-witted gardener looking up at me with open mouth, and the atrabilious confectioner clap his hands, which made me take refuge in my paper again. I got to the end of my task without any remarkable incident, if I except the doctor's once calling out "hear" loudly, which brought the heart into my mouth, and blurred half a sentence. When I sat down, there were the usual sounds of approbation, and the confectioner returned thanks in the name of the audience.

ON VAGABONDS

BEING A DISCOURSE DELIVERED BEFORE THE
DREAMTHORP LITERARY INSTITUTE, SESSION
1862–63

CALL it oddity, eccentricity, humour, or what
you please, it is evident that the special
flavour of mind or manner, which, independently
of fortune, station, or profession, sets a man apart
and makes him distinguishable from his fellows,
and which gives the charm of picturesqueness to
society, is fast disappearing from amongst us.
A man may count the odd people of his acquaintance on his fingers; and it is observable that these
odd people are generally well stricken in years.
They belong more to the past generation than to
the present. Our young men are terribly alike.
For these many years back the young gentlemen
I have had the fortune to encounter are clever,
knowing, selfish, disagreeable; the young ladies
are of one pattern like minted sovereigns of the
same reign—excellent gold, I have no doubt, but
each bearing the same awfully proper image and

[270]

superscription. There are no blanks in the matrimonial lottery now-a-days, but the prizes are all of a value, and there is but one kind of article given for the ticket. Courtship is an absurdity, and a sheer waste of time. If a man could but close his eyes in a ball-room, dash into a bevy of muslin beauties, carry off the fair one that accident gives to his arms, his raid would be as reasonable and as likely to produce happiness as the more ordinary methods of procuring a spouse. If a man has to choose one guinea out of a bag containing one hundred and fifty, what can he do? What wonderful wisdom can he display in his choice? There is no appreciable difference of value in the golden pieces. The latest coined are a little fresher, that's all. An Act of Uniformity, with heavy penalties for recusants, seems to have been passed upon the English race. That we can quite well account for this state of things, does not make the matter better, does not make it the less our duty to fight against it. We are apt to be told that men are too busy and women too accomplished for humour of speech or originality of character or manner. In the truth of this lies the pity of it. If, with the exceptions of hedges that divide fields, and streams that run as marches between farms, every inch of soil were drained, ploughed, manured, and under that improved cultivation rushing up into astonishing wheaten and oaten crops, enriching tenant and proprietor, the aspect of the country would be decidedly uninteresting, and would present scant attraction to the man riding or walking through it. In such a world the tourists would be few. Personally, I should detest a world all red and ruled with the ploughshare in spring, all covered with harvest in autumn. I wish a little variety. I desiderate moors and barren places; the copse where you can flush the woodcock; the warren where, when you approach, you can see the twinkle of innumerable rabbit tails; and, to tell the truth, would not feel sorry although Reynard himself had a hole beneath the wooded bank, even if the demands of his rising family cost Farmer Yellowleas a fat capon or two in the season. The fresh, rough, heathery parts of human nature, where the air is freshest, and where the linnets sing, is getting encroached upon by cultivated fields. Every one is making himself and herself useful. Every one is producing something. Everybody is clever. Everybody is a philanthropist. I don't like it. I love a little eccentricity. I respect honest prejudices. I admire foolish enthusiasm in a young head better than a wise scepticism. It is high time, it seems to me, that a moral game-law were passed for the preservation of the wild and vagrant feelings of human nature.

I have advertised myself to speak of *vagabonds*, and I must explain what I mean by the term. We all know what was the doom of the first child born of man, and it is needless for me to say that I do not wish the spirit of Cain more widely

diffused amongst my fellow-creatures. By vagabond, I do not mean a tramp, or a gipsy, or a
thimblerigger, or a brawler who is brought up
with a black eye before a magistrate of a morning.
The vagabond as I have him in my mind's eye,
and whom I dearly love, comes out of quite a
different mould. The man I speak of seldom,
it is true, attains to the dignity of a church-
warden; he is never found sitting at a reformed
town-council board; he has a horror of public
platforms; he never by any chance heads a sub-
scription list with a donation of fifty pounds. On
the other hand, he is very far from being a "ne'er-
do-weel," as the Scotch phrase it, or an imprudent
person. He does not play at "Aunt Sally" on a
public race-course; he does not wrench knockers
from the doors of slumbering citizens; he has never
seen the interior of a police cell. It is quite true,
he has a peculiar way of looking at many things.
If, for instance, he is brought up with cousin
Milly, and loves her dearly, and the childish affection grows up and strengthens in the woman's
heart, and there is a fair chance for them fighting
the world side by side, he marries her without too
curiously considering whether his income will per-
mit him to give dinner-parties, and otherwise
fashionably see his friends. Very imprudent, no
doubt. But you cannot convince my vagabond.
With the strangest logical twist, which seems
natural to him, he conceives that he marries for
his own sake, and not for the sake of his acquaint-

ances, and that the possession of a loving heart and a conscience void of reproach, is worth, at any time, an odd sovereign in his pocket. The vagabond is not a favourite with the respectable classes. He is particularly feared by mammas who have daughters to dispose of—not that he is a bad son, or likely to prove a bad husband, or a treacherous friend, but somehow gold does not stick to his fingers as it does to the fingers of some men. He is regardless of appearances. He chooses his friends neither for their fine houses nor their rare wines, but for their humours, their goodness of heart, their capacities of making a joke and of seeing one, and for their abilities, unknown often as the woodland violet, but not the less sweet for obscurity. As a consequence his acquaintance is miscellaneous, and he is often seen at other places than rich men's feasts. I do believe he is a gainer by reason of his vagrant ways. He comes in contact with the queer corners and the out-of-the-way places of human life. He knows more of our common nature, just as the man who walks through a country, and who strikes off the main road now and then to visit a ruin, or a legendary cairn of stones, who drops into village inns, and talks with the people he meets on the road, becomes better acquainted with it than the man who rolls haughtily along the turnpike in a carriage and four. We lose a great deal by foolish hauteur. No man is worth much who has not a touch of the vagabond in him. Could I have visited London

[274]

thirty years ago, I would rather have spent an hour with Charles Lamb than with any other of its residents. He was a fine specimen of the vagabond, as I conceive him. His mind was as full of queer nooks and tortuous passages as any mansion-house of Elizabeth's day or earlier, where the rooms are cosy, albeit a little low in the roof; where dusty stained lights are falling on old oaken panelings; where every bit of furniture has a reverent flavour of ancientness; where portraits of noble men and women, all dead long ago, are hanging on the walls; and where a black-letter Chaucer with silver clasps is lying open on a seat in the window. There was nothing modern about him. The garden of his mind did not flaunt in gay parterres; it resembled those that Cowley and Evelyn delighted in, with clipped trees, and shaven lawns, and stone satyrs, and dark, shadowing yews, and a sun-dial with a Latin motto sculptured on it, standing at the farther end. Lamb was the slave of quip and whimsey; he stuttered out puns to the detriment of all serious and improving conversation, and twice or so in the year he was overtaken in liquor. Well, in spite of these things, perhaps on account of these things, I love his memory. For love and charity ripened in that nature as peaches ripen on the wall that fronts the sun. Although he did not blow his trumpet in the corners of the streets, he was tried, as few men are, and fell not. He jested that he might not weep. He wore a martyr's heart beneath his suit of

motley. And only years after his death, when to
admiration or censure he was alike insensible, did
the world know his story, and that of his sister
Mary.

Ah, me! what a world this was to live in two or
three centuries ago, when it was getting itself discovered—when the sunset gave up America, when
a steel hand had the spoiling of Mexico and Peru!
Then were the "Arabian Nights" commonplace,
enchantments a matter of course, and romance
the most ordinary thing in the world. Then man
was courting Nature, now he has married her.
Every mystery is dissipated. The planet is familiar
as the trodden pathway running between towns.
We no longer gaze wistfully to the west, dreaming
of the Fortunate Isles. We seek our wonders now
on the ebbed sea-shore; we discover our new
worlds with the microscope. Yet, for all that time
has brought and taken away, I am glad to know
that the vagabond sleeps in our blood and awakes
now and then. Overlay human nature as you
please, here and there some bit of rock, or mound
of aboriginal soil, will crop out with the wild
flowers growing upon it, sweetening the air. When
the boy throws his Delectus or his Euclid aside,
and takes passionately to the reading of "Robinson Crusoe" or Bruce's "African Travels," do
not shake your head despondingly over him and
prophesy evil issues. Let the wild hawk try its
wings. It will be hooded, and will sit quietly
enough on the falconer's perch ere long. Let the

wild horse career over its boundless pampas; the
jerk of the lasso will bring it down soon enough.
Soon enough will the snaffle in the mouth and the
spur of the tamer subdue the high spirit to the
bridle, or the carriage-trace. Perhaps not, and if
so, the better for all parties. Once more there
will be a new man and new deeds in the world. For
Genius is a vagabond, Art is a vagabond, Enter-
prise is a vagabond. Vagabonds have moulded
the world into its present shape; they have made
the houses in which we dwell, the roads on which
we ride and drive, the very laws that govern us.
Respectable people swarm in the track of the
vagabond as rooks in the track of the ploughshare.
Respectable people do little in the world except
storing wine-cellars and amassing fortunes for the
benefit of spendthrift heirs. Respectable well-to-
do Grecians shook their heads over Leonidas and
his three hundred when they went down to Ther-
mopylae. Respectable Spanish churchmen with
shaven crowns scouted the dream of Columbus.
Respectable German folks attempted to dissuade
Luther from appearing before Charles and the
princes and electors of the empire, and were
scandalised when he declared that "were there as
many devils in Worms as there were tiles on the
house-tops, still would he on." Nature makes us
vagabonds, the world makes us respectable.

In the fine sense in which I take the word, the
English are the greatest vagabonds on the earth,
and it is the healthiest trait in their national

character. The first fine day in spring awakes the
gipsy in the blood of the English workman, and
incontinently he "babbles of green fields." On
the English gentleman, lapped in the most luxurious civilisation, and with the thousand powers
and resources of wealth at his command, descends
oftentimes a fierce unrest, a Bedouin-like horror
of cities and the cry of the money-changer, and
in a month the fiery dust rises in the track of his
desert steed, or in the six months' polar midnight
he hears the big wave clashing on the icy shore.
The close presence of the sea feeds the Englishman's restlessness. She takes possession of his
heart like some fair capricious mistress. Before
the boy awakes to the beauty of Cousin Mary,
he is crazed by the fascinations of ocean. With her
voices of ebb and flow she weaves her siren song
round the Englishman's coasts day and night.
Nothing that dwells on land can keep from her
embrace the boy who has gazed upon her dangerous beauty, and who has heard her singing songs of
foreign shores at the foot of the summer crag. It
is well that in the modern gentleman the fierce
heart of the Berserker lives yet. The English are
eminently a nation of vagabonds. The sun paints
English faces with all the colours of his climes.
The Englishman is ubiquitous. He shakes with
fever and ague in the swampy valley of the Mis-
sissippi; he is drowned in the sand pillars as they
waltz across the desert on the purple breath of
the simoom; he stands on the icy scalp of Mont

Blanc; his fly falls in the sullen Norwegian fiords;
he invades the solitude of the Cape lion; he rides
on his donkey through the uncausewayed Cairo
streets. That wealthy people, under a despotism,
should be travellers seems a natural thing enough.
It is a way of escape from the rigours of their
condition. But that England—where activity
rages so keenly and engrosses every class; where
the prizes of Parliament, literature, commerce,
the Bar, the Church, are hungered and thirsted
after; where the stress and intensity of life ages
a man before his time; where so many of the
noblest break down in harness hardly half-way
to the goal—should, year after year, send off
swarms of men to roam the world, and to seek out
danger for the mere thrill and enjoyment of it, is
significant of the indomitable pluck and spirit of
the race. There is scant danger that the rust of
sloth will eat into the virtue of English steel. The
English do the hard work and the travelling of
the world. The least revolutionary nation of Europe, the one with the greatest temptations to
stay at home, with the greatest faculty for work,
with perhaps the sincerest regard for wealth, is
also the most nomadic. How is this? It is because
they are a nation of vagabonds; they have the
"hungry heart" that one of their poets speaks
about.

There is an amiability about the genuine vagabond which takes captive the heart. We do not
love a man for his respectability, his prudence

and foresight in business, his capacity of living
within his income, or his balance at his banker's.
We all admit that prudence is an admirable virtue, and occasionally lament, about Christmas,
when bills fall in, that we do not inherit it in a
greater degree. But we speak about it in quite a
cool way. It does not touch us with enthusiasm.
If a calculating-machine had a hand to wring, it
would find few to wring it warmly. The things
that really move liking in human beings are the
gnarled nodosities of character, vagrant humours,
freaks of generosity, some little unextinguishable
spark of the aboriginal savage, some little sweet
savour of the old Adam. It is quite wonderful
how far simple generosity and kindliness of heart
go in securing affection; and, when these exist,
what a host of apologists spring up for faults and
vices even! A country squire goes recklessly to
the dogs, yet if he has a kind word for his tenant
when he meets him, a frank greeting for the rustic
beauty when she drops a curtsy to him on the highway, he lives for a whole generation in an odour
of sanctity. If he had been a disdainful, hook-
nosed prime minister, who had carried his country
triumphantly through some frightful crisis of war,
these people would, perhaps, never have been
aware of the fact; and most certainly never
would have tendered him a word of thanks, even
if they had. When that important question,
"Which is the greatest foe to the public weal—
the miser or the spendthrift?" is discussed at the

artisans' debating club, the spendthrift has all
the eloquence on his side—the miser all the votes.
The miser's advocate is nowhere, and he pleads
the cause of his client with only half his heart.
In the theatre, Charles Surface is applauded, and
Joseph Surface is hissed. The novel-reader's affection goes out to Tom Jones, his hatred to Blifil.
Joseph Surface and Blifil are scoundrels, it is true,
but deduct the scoundrelism, let Joseph be but a
stale proverb-monger and Blifil a conceited prig,
and the issue remains the same. Good humour
and generosity carry the day with the popular
heart all the world over. Tom Jones and Charles
Surface are not vagabonds to my taste. They
were shabby fellows both, and were treated a
great deal too well. But there are other vagabonds
whom I love, and whom I do well to love. With
what affection do I follow little Ishmael and his
broken-hearted mother out into the great and
terrible wilderness, and see them faint beneath
the ardours of the sunlight. And we feel it to be
strict poetic justice and compensation, that the lad
so driven forth from human tents should become
the father of wild Arabian men, to whom the air
of cities is poison, who work not with any tool,
and on whose limbs no conqueror has ever yet
been able to rivet shackle or chain. Then there are
Abraham's grandchildren, Jacob and Esau—the
former, I confess, no favourite of mine. His, up
at least to his closing years, when parental affection and strong sorrow softened him, was a char-

acter not amiable. He lacked generosity, and had too keen an eye on his own advancement. He did not inherit the noble strain of his ancestors. He was a prosperous man; yet in spite of his increase in flocks and herds, in spite of his vision of the ladder with the angels ascending and descending upon it, in spite of the success of his beloved son, in spite of the weeping and lamentation of the Egyptians at his death, in spite of his splendid funeral, winding from the city by the pyramid and the sphinx—in spite of all these things, I would rather have been the hunter Esau, with birthright filched away, bankrupt in the promise, rich only in fleet foot and keen spear; for he carried into the wilds with him an essentially noble nature—no brother with his mess of pottage could mulct him of that. And he had a fine revenge; for, when Jacob, on his journey, heard that his brother was near with four hundred men, and made division of his flocks and herds, his man-servants and maid-servants, impetuous as a swollen hill-torrent, the fierce son of the desert, baked red with Syrian light, leaped down upon him, and fell on his neck and wept. And Esau said, "What meanest thou by all this drove which I met?" and Jacob said, "These are to find grace in the sight of my lord"; then Esau said, "I have enough, my brother; keep that thou hast unto thyself." O mighty prince, didst thou remember thy mother's guile, the skins upon thy hands and neck, and the lie put upon the patriarch, as, blind with years,

he sat up in his bed snuffing the savoury meat?
An ugly memory, I should fancy!

Commend me to Shakspeare's vagabonds, the
most delightful in the world! His sweet-blooded
and liberal nature blossomed into all fine generosities as naturally as an apple-bough into pink-
blossoms and odours. Listen to Gonsalo talking
to the shipwrecked Milan nobles camped for the
night in Prospero's isle, full of sweet voices, with
Ariel shooting through the enchanted air like
a falling star:—

Had I the plantation of this isle, my lord,
I' the commonwealth I would by contraries
Execute all things; for no kind of traffic
Would I admit; no name of magistrate;
Letters should not be known; riches, poverty,
And use of service none; contract, succession,
Bourne, bound of land, tilth, title, vineyard none;
No use of metal coin, or wine, or oil;
No occupation—all men idle—all!
And women too, but innocent and pure;
No sovereignty;
All things in common nature should produce,
Without sweat or endurance; treason, felony,
Sword, pike, knife, gun, or need of any engine
Would I not have; but nature would bring forth
Of its own kind all foison, all abundance,
To feed my innocent people.
I would with such perfection govern, sir,
To excel the golden age.

[283]

What think you of a world after that pattern?
"As You Like It" is a vagabond play, and verily,
if there waved in any wind that blows a forest
peopled like Arden's, with an exiled king drawing
the sweetest humanest lessons from misfortune;
a melancholy Jacques, stretched by the river bank,
moralising on the bleeding deer; a fair Rosalind,
chanting her saucy cuckoo song; fools like Touch-
stone—not like those of our acquaintance, my
friends; and the whole place, from centre to cir-
cumference, filled with mighty oak boles, all carven
with lovers' names—if such a forest waved in
wind, I say, I would, be my worldly prospects
what they might, pack up at once, and cast in
my lot with that vagabond company. For there
I should find more gallant courtesies, finer sentiments, completer innocence and happiness, more
wit and wisdom, than I am like to do here even,
though I search for them from shepherd's cot to
king's palace. Just to think how those people
lived! Carelessly as the blossoming trees, happily
as the singing birds, time measured only by the
patter of the acorn on the fruitful soil! A world
without debtor or creditor, passing rich, yet with
never a doit in its purse, with no sordid care, no
regard for appearances; nothing to occupy the
young but love-making, nothing to occupy the old
but perusing the "sermons in stones" and the
musical wisdom which dwells in "running brooks!"
But Arden forest draws its sustenance from a
poet's brain: the light that sleeps on its leafy

pillows is "the light that never was on sea or shore." We but please and tantalise ourselves with beautiful dreams.

The children of the brain become to us actual existences, more actual indeed than the people who impinge upon us in the street, or who live next door. We are more intimate with Shakspeare's men and women than we are with our contemporaries, and they are, on the whole, better company. They are more beautiful in form and feature, and they express themselves in a way that the most gifted strive after in vain. What if Shakspeare's people could walk out of the play-books and settle down upon some spot of earth and conduct life there! There would be found humanity's whitest wheat, the world's unalloyed gold. The very winds could not visit the place roughly. No king's court could present you such an array. Where else could we find a philosopher like Hamlet? a friend like Antonio? a witty fellow like Mercutio? where else Imogen's piquant face? Portia's gravity and womanly sweetness? Rosalind's true heart and silvery laughter? Cordelia's beauty of holiness? These would form the centre of the court, but the purlieus, how many-coloured! Malvolio would walk mincingly in the sunshine there; Autolycus would filch purses. Sir Andrew Aguecheek and Sir Toby Belch would be eternal boon companions. And as Falstaff sets out homeward from the tavern, the portly knight leading the revellers like a three-decker a line of frigates,

they are encountered by Dogberry, who summons
them to stand and answer to the watch as they
are honest men. If Mr. Dickens's characters were
gathered together, they would constitute a town
populous enough to send a representative to Parliament. Let us enter. The style of architecture is
unparalleled. There is an individuality about the
buildings. In some obscure way they remind one
of human faces. There are houses sly-looking,
houses wicked-looking, houses pompous-looking.
Heaven bless us! what a rakish pump! what a self-
important town-hall! what a hard-hearted prison!
The dead walls are covered with advertisements
of Mr. Slearey's circus. Newman Noggs comes
shambling along. Mr. and the Misses Pecksniff
come sailing down the sunny side of the street.
Miss Mercy's parasol is gay; papa's neckcloth is
white, and terribly starched. Dick Swiveller leans
against a wall, his hands in his pockets, a primrose
held between his teeth, contemplating the opera
of Punch and Judy, which is being conducted
under the management of Messrs. Codlin and
Short. You turn a corner and you meet the coffin
of little Paul Dombey borne along. Who would
have thought of encountering a funeral in this
place? In the afternoon you hear the rich tones
of the organ from Miss La Creevy's first floor, for
Tom Pinch has gone to live there now; and as you
know all the people as you know your own brothers and sisters, and consequently require no letters
of introduction, you go up and talk with the dear

old fellow about all his friends and your friends, and towards evening he takes your arm, and you walk out to see poor Nelly's grave—a place which he visits often, and which he dresses with flowers with his own hands. I know this is the idlest dreaming, but all of us have a sympathy with the creatures of the drama and the novel. Around the hardest cark and toil lies the imaginative world of the poets and romancists, and thither we sometimes escape to snatch a mouthful of serener air. There our best lost feelings have taken a human shape. We suppose that boyhood with its impulses and enthusiasms has subsided with the gray cynical man whom we have known these many years. Not a bit of it. It has escaped into the world of the poet, and walks a love-flushed Romeo in immortal youth. We suppose that the Mary of fifty years since, the rose-bud of a girl that crazed our hearts, blossomed into the spouse of Jenkins, the stockbroker, and is now a grandmother. Not at all. She is Juliet leaning from the balcony, or Portia talking on the moonlight lawns at Belmont. There walk the shadows of our former selves. All that Time steals he takes thither; and to live in that world is to live in our lost youth, our lost generosities, illusions, and romances.

In middle-class life, and in the professions, when a standard or ideal is tacitly set up, to which every member is expected to conform on pain of having himself talked about, and wise heads shaken over him, the quick feelings of the vagabond are not

frequently found. Yet, thanks to Nature! who
sends her leafage and flowerage up through all
kinds of *débris*, and who takes a blossomy possession of ruined walls and desert places, it is never
altogether dead. And of vagabonds not the least
delightful is he who retains poetry and boyish
spirits beneath the crust of a profession. Mr.
Carlyle commends "central fire," and very properly commends it most when "well covered in."
In the case of a professional man, this "central
fire" does not manifest itself in wasteful explosiveness, but in secret genial heat visible in fruits of
charity and pleasant humour. The physician who
is a humorist commends himself doubly to a sick-
bed. His patients are as much indebted for their
cure to his smile, his voice, and a certain irresistible healthfulness that surrounds him, as they
are to his skill and his prescriptions. The lawyer
who is a humorist is a man of ten thousand. How
easily the worldly-wise face puckered over a stiff
brief relaxes into the lines of laughter. He sees
many an evil side of human nature, he is familiar
with slanders and injustice, all kinds of human
bitterness and falsity; but neither his hand nor
his heart becomes "embued with that it works
in"; and the little admixture of acid, inevitable
from his circumstances and mode of life, but
heightens the flavour of his humour. But of all
humorists of the professional class, I prefer the
clergyman, expecially if he is well stricken in
years, and has been anchored all his life in a

country charge. He is none of your loud wits. There is a lady-like delicacy in his mind, a constant sense of his holy office which warn him off dangerous subjects. This reserve, however, does but improve the quality of his mirth. What his humour loses in boldness it gains in depth and slyness. And as the good man has seldom the opportunity of making a joke, or of procuring an auditor who can understand one, the dewy glitter of his eyes, as you sit opposite him, and his heartfelt enjoyment of the matter in hand, are worth going a considerable way to witness. It is not, however, in the professions that the vagabond is commonly found. Over these that awful and ubiquitous female, Mrs. Grundy—at once Fate, Nemesis, and Fury—presides. The glare of her eye is professional danger, the pointing of her finger is professional death. When she utters a man's name he is lost. The true vagabond is to be met with in other walks of life—among actors, poets, painters. These may grow in any way their nature directs. They are not required to conform to any traditional pattern. With regard to the respectabilities and the "minor morals," the world permits them to be libertines. Besides, it is a temperament peculiarly sensitive, or generous, or enjoying, which at the beginning impels these to their special pursuits; and that temperament, like everything else in the world, strengthens with use, and grows with what it feeds on. We look upon an actor, sitting amongst ordinary men and women, with a certain curiosity—we regard him as a creature from another planet, almost. His life and his world are quite different from ours. The orchestra, the footlights, and the green baize curtain divide us. He is a monarch half his time —his entrance and his exit proclaimed by flourish of trumpet. He speaks in blank verse, is wont to take his seat at gilded banquets, to drink nothing out of a pasteboard goblet. The actor's world has a history amusing to read, and lines of noble and splendid traditions, stretching back to charming Nelly's time and earlier. The actor has strange experiences. He sees the other side of the moon. We roar at Grimaldi's funny face: he sees the lines of pain in it. We hear Romeo wish to be "a glove upon that hand, that he might touch that cheek"; three minutes afterwards he beholds Romeo refresh himself with a pot of porter. We see the Moor, who "loved not wisely but too well," smother Desdemona with the nuptial bolster: he sees them sit down to a hot supper. We always think of the actor as on the stage: he always thinks of us as in the boxes. In justice to the poets of the present day, it may be noticed that they have improved on their brethren in Johnson's time, who were, according to Lord Macaulay, hunted by bailiffs and familiar with sponging-houses, and who, when hospitably entertained, were wont to disturb the household of the entertainer by roaring for hot punch at four o'clock in the morning. Since that period the poets have

improved in the decencies of life: they wear broadcloth, and settle their tailors' accounts even as
other men. At this present moment her Majesty's
poets are perhaps the most respectable of her
Majesty's subjects. They are all teetotallers; if
they sin, it is in rhyme, and then only to point
a moral. In past days the poet flew from flower
to flower gathering his honey, but he bore a sting,
too, as the rude hand that touched him could
testify. He freely gathers his honey as of old, but
the satiric sting has been taken away. He lives at
peace with all men—his brethren excepted. About
the true poet still there is something of the ancient
spirit—the old "flash and outbreak of the fiery
mind"—the old enthusiasm and dash of humorous
eccentricity. But he is fast disappearing from the
catalogue of vagabonds—fast getting commonplace, I fear. Many people suspect him of dulness.
Besides, such a crowd of well-meaning, amiable,
most respectable men have broken down of late
years the pales of Parnassus, and become squatters
on the sacred mount, that the claim of poets to
be a peculiar people is getting disallowed. Never
in this world's history were they so numerous;
and although some people deny that they *are*
poets, few are cantankerous enough or intrepid
enough to assert that they are vagabonds. The
painter is the most agreeable of vagabonds. His
art is a pleasant one: it demands some little manual
exertion, and it takes him at times into the open
air. It is pleasant, too, in this, that lines and

colours are so much more palpable than words,
and the appeal of his work to his practised eye has
some satisfaction in it. He knows what he is
about. He does not altogether lose his critical
sense, as the poet does, when familiarity stales
his subject, and takes the splendour out of his
images. Moreover, his work is more profitable
than the poet's. I suppose there are just as few
great painters at the present day as there are great
poets; yet the yearly receipts of the artists of
England far exceed the receipts of the singers.
A picture can usually be painted in less time than
a poem can be written. A second-rate picture has
a certain market value—its frame is at least something. A second-rate poem is utterly worthless,
and no one will buy it on account of its binding.
A picture is your own exclusive property: it is
a costly article of furniture. You hang it on your
walls to be admired by all the world. Pictures
represent wealth: the possession of them is a luxury. The portrait-painter is of all men the most
beloved. You sit to him willingly, and put on
your best looks. You are inclined to be pleased
with his work, on account of the strong prepossess-
sion you entertain for his subject. To sit for one's
portrait is like being present at one's own creation.
It is an admirable excuse for egotism. You would
not discourse of the falcon-like curve which dis-
tinguishes your nose, or the sweet serenity of your
reposing lips, or the mildness of the eye that
spreads a light over your countenance, in the

presence of a fellow-creature for the whole world, yet you do not hesitate to express the most favourable opinion of the features starting out on you from the wet canvas. The interest the painter takes in his task flatters you. And when the sittings are over, and you behold yourself hanging on your own wall, looking as if you could direct kingdoms or lead armies, you feel grateful to the artist. He ministers to your self-love, and you pay him his hire without wincing. Your heart warms towards him as it would towards a poet who addresses you in an ode of panegyric, the kindling terms of which—a little astonishing to your friends —you believe in your heart of hearts to be the simple truth, and, in the matter of expression, not over-coloured in the very least. The portrait-painter has a shrewd eye for character, and is usually the best anecdote-monger in the world. His craft brings him into contact with many faces, and he learns to compare them curiously, and to extract their meanings. He can interpret wrinkles; he can look through the eyes into the man; he can read a whole foregone history in the lines about the mouth. Besides, from the good understanding which usually exists between the artist and his sitter, the latter is inclined somewhat to unbosom himself; little things leak out in conversation, not much in themselves, but pregnant enough to the painter's sense, who pieces them together, and constitutes a tolerably definite image. The man who paints your face knows you

better than your intimate friends do, and has a
clearer knowledge of your amiable weaknesses,
and of the secret motives which influence your
conduct, than you oftentimes have yourself. A
good portrait is a kind of biography, and neither
painter nor biographer can carry out his task
satisfactorily unless he be admitted behind the
scenes. I think that the landscape-painter who
has acquired sufficient mastery in his art to
satisfy his own critical sense, and who is appreciated enough to find purchasers, and thereby
to keep the wolf from the door, must be of all
mankind the happiest. Other men live in cities,
bound down to some settled task and order of
life, but he is a nomad, and wherever he goes
"Beauty pitches her tents before him." He is
smitten by a passionate love for Nature, and is
privileged to follow her into her solitary haunts
and recesses. Nature is his mistress, and he is
continually making declarations of his love. When
one thinks of ordinary occupations, how one
envies him, flecking his oak-tree bole with sunlight, tinging with rose the cloud of the morning
in which the lark is hid, making the sea's swift
fringe of foaming lace outspread itself on the
level sands, in which the pebbles gleam for ever
wet. The landscape-painter's memory is inhabited
by the fairest visions—dawn burning on the splintered peaks that the eagles know, while the valleys
beneath are yet filled with uncertain light—the
bright-blue morn stretching over miles of moor

and mountain—the slow up-gathering of the bellied thunder-cloud—summer lakes, and cattle knee-deep in them—rustic bridges for ever crossed by old women in scarlet cloaks—old-fashioned waggons resting on the scrubby common, the waggoner lazy and way-worn, the dog couched on the ground, its tongue hanging out in the heat —boats drawn up on the shore at sunset; the fisher's children looking seawards, the red light full on their dresses and faces; farther back, a clump of cottages, with bait-baskets about the door, and the smoke of the evening meal coiling up into the coloured air. These things are for ever with him. Beauty, which is a luxury to other men, is his daily food. Happy vagabond, who lives the whole summer through in the light of his mistress's face, and who does nothing the whole winter except recall the splendour of her smiles!

The vagabond, as I have explained and sketched him, is not a man to tremble at, or avoid as if he wore contagion in his touch. He is upright, generous, innocent, is conscientious in the performance of his duties; and if a little eccentric and fond of the open air, he is full of good nature and mirthful charity. He may not make money so rapidly as you do, but I cannot help thinking that he enjoys life a great deal more. The quick feeling of life, the exuberance of animal spirits which break out in the traveller, the sportsman, the poet, the painter, should be more generally diffused. We should be all the better and all the happier for it. Life ought to be freer, heartier, more enjoyable than it is at present. If the professional fetter must be worn, let it be worn as lightly as possible. It should never be permitted to canker the limbs. We are a free people—we have an unshackled Press—we have an open platform, and can say our say upon it, no king or despot making us afraid. We send representatives to Parliament; the franchise is always going to be extended. All this is very fine, and we do well to glory in our privileges as Britons. But, although we enjoy greater political freedom than any other people, we are the victims of a petty social tyranny. We are our own despots —we tremble at a neighbour's whisper. A man may say what he likes on a public platform—he may publish whatever opinion he chooses—but he dare not wear a peculiar fashion of hat on the street. Eccentricity is an outlaw. Public opinion blows like the east wind, blighting bud and blossom on the human bough. As a consequence of all this, society is losing picturesqueness and variety—we are all growing up after one pattern. In other matters than architecture past times may be represented by the wonderful ridge of the Old Town of Edinburgh, where everything is individual and characteristic: the present time by the streets and squares of the New Town, where everything is gray, cold, and respectable; where every house is the other's *alter ego*. It is true that life is healthier in the formal square than in the piled-up picturesqueness of the Canongate, quite true that sanitary conditions are better observed—that pure water flows through every tenement like blood through a human body, that daylight has free access, and that the apartments are larger and higher in the roof. But every gain is purchased at the expense of some loss; and it is best to combine, if possible, the excellences of the old and the new. By all means retain the modern breadth of light and range of space, by all means have water plentiful and bed-chambers ventilated, but at the same time have some little freak of fancy without—some ornament about the door, some device about the window—something to break the cold, gray, stony uniformity; or, to leave metaphor, which is always dangerous ground —for I really don't wish to advocate Ruskinism and the Gothic—it would be better to have, along with our modern enlightenment, our higher tastes and purer habits, a greater individuality of thought and manner; better, while retaining all that we have gained, that harmless eccentricity should be respected—that every man should be allowed to grow in his own way, so long as he does not infringe on the rights of his neighbour, or insolently thrust himself between him and the sun. A little more air and light should be let in upon life. I should think the world has stood long enough under the drill of Adjutant Fashion. It is hard work; the posture is wearisome, and Fashion is an awful martinet, and has a quick eye, and comes down mercilessly on the unfortunate wight who cannot square his toes to the approved pattern, or who appears upon parade with a darn in his coat, or with a shoulder-belt insufficiently pipeclayed. It is killing work. Suppose we try "standing at ease" for a little!

THE END